CGP is No. 1 for number skills!

There are some number skills that are absolutely <u>essential</u> for KS3 Maths —
and CGP's Catch-Up Maths Workbooks will help you master them all.

Each book is packed with mixed practice to build your confidence,
with plenty of clear study notes and examples to help you get started.
Every skill is revisited regularly to make sure everything's sinking in.

This is Workbook 2 of 5. Turn to the last page for more info
about what's covered in the other four Workbooks!

CGP — still the best! ☺

Our sole aim here at CGP is to produce the highest quality books —
carefully written, immaculately presented and dangerously close to being funny.

Then we work our socks off to get them out to you
— at the cheapest possible prices.

Contents

Published by CGP

ISBN: 978 1 78908 059 9

Editors: Laura Collins, Samuel Mann, Ben Train, Dawn Wright

With thanks to Mike Ollerton for the reviewing.
With thanks to Sammy El-Bahrawy, Rosie Hanson and Mark Moody for the proofreading.

Please note that CGP and the KS3 Catch-Up Maths range are in no way associated with, or endorsed by, The Caxton Trust or the Catch Up Numeracy and Literacy intervention schemes offered by The Caxton Trust.

Clipart from Corel®
Printed by Elanders Ltd, Newcastle upon Tyne.

Based on the classic CGP style created by Richard Parsons.

How 'Catch-Up Maths' Works

This book is designed to improve number fluency by building up number facts in students' long-term memory. This frees up space in their working memory, which they can then use for problem-solving.

'Interleaving' and 'Spacing'

'Catch-Up Maths' uses a new approach which has been shown to boost students' long-term memory:

- Topics are INTERLEAVED — students practise several topics in one exercise, instead of repeatedly practising the same thing. This helps students learn to choose appropriate methods for tackling different types of problems.

- Practice on each topic is SPACED through the books at increasing intervals. Recalling content which is not fresh in students' minds has been shown to improve learning.

How the Exercises are structured

Just one new concept is introduced in each Exercise.

Question 1 gives students practice at the new concept.

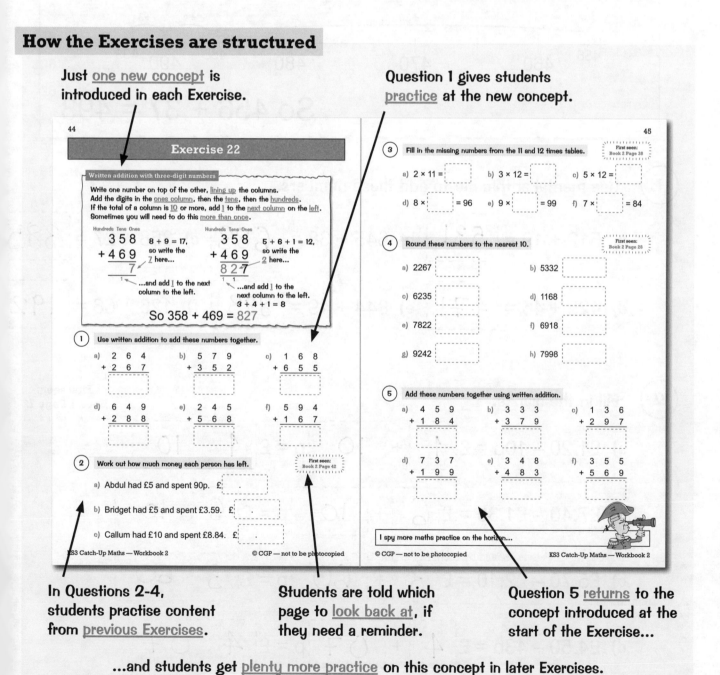

In Questions 2-4, students practise content from previous Exercises.

Students are told which page to look back at, if they need a reminder.

Question 5 returns to the concept introduced at the start of the Exercise...

...and students get plenty more practice on this concept in later Exercises.

Exercise 1

Mental addition with three-digit and two-digit numbers

Partition the two-digit number into <u>tens</u> and <u>ones</u>. Then add them <u>separately</u>.

$$456 + 37 = ?$$

$37 = \underline{3 \text{ tens}} + \underline{7 \text{ ones}}$

$$45\underline{6} + \underline{3}0 = 4\underline{8}6 \qquad 4\underline{86} + \underline{7} = 4\underline{93}$$

Add <u>3 tens</u> to
the tens column...

...then add
the <u>7 ones</u>.

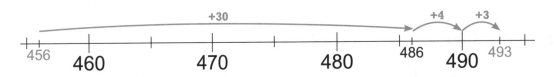

So 456 + 37 = 493

1) Use mental arithmetic to add these numbers. ✓6

a) 512 + 19 = `531`   b) 645 + 38 = `683`   c) 358 + 27 = `385`

d) 425 + 46 = `471`   e) 844 + 49 = `893`   f) 126 + 66 = `192`

2) Fill in the blanks. ✓4

First seen:
Book 1 Page 72

a) £1.20 − 10p = £ `1` + `10` p = £ `1` . `10`

b) £7.40 − £1.30 = £ `6` + `10` p = £ `6` . `10`

c) £5.70 − £2.10 = £ `3` + `60` p = £ `3` . `60`

d) £4.50 − 43p = £ `4` + `07` p = £ `4` . `07`

(3) Write true or false for each of these statements. ✓5

First seen: Book 1 Page 46

a) 334 rounded to the nearest 10 is 340   True

b) 216 rounded to the nearest 10 is 220   True

c) 571 rounded to the nearest 10 is 570   ~~False~~ True

d) 835 rounded to the nearest 10 is 830   False

e) 999 rounded to the nearest 10 is 990   False

(4) Fill in the missing numbers. ✓9

First seen: Book 1 Page 68

a) 616 – 13 = 603   b) 549 – 32 = 517   c) 756 – 23 = 733

d) 294 – 52 = 242   e) 475 – 42 = 433   f) 268 – 57 = 211

g) 958 – 24 = 934   h) 869 – 48 = 821   i) 386 – 72 = 314

(5) Add these numbers together using mental arithmetic. ✓9

a) 644 + 28 = 672   b) 329 + 57 = 386   c) 266 + 25 = 291

d) 778 + 14 = 792   e) 543 + 28 = 571   f) 439 + 49 = 488

g) 214 + 67 = 281   h) 347 + 46 = 393   i) 818 + 33 = 851

Why not sit down and take a break...

Exercise 2

Mental division using the times tables

The <u>times tables</u> can be used to <u>divide</u> numbers.

$$8 \times 3 = 24$$

So 24 divides into <u>3 groups of 8</u>...

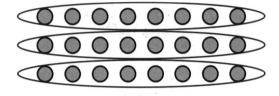

$$24 \div 3 = 8$$

...and <u>8 groups of 3</u>.

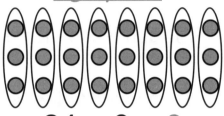

$$24 \div 8 = 3$$

(1) Use the 2, 3 and 4 times tables to fill in the blanks.

✓9

a) $2 \times 4 = 8$

$8 \div 2 = \boxed{4}$

b) $3 \times 3 = 9$

$9 \div 3 = \boxed{3}$

c) $5 \times 2 = 10$

$10 \div 5 = \boxed{2}$

d) $11 \times 4 = 44$

$44 \div 11 = \boxed{4}$

e) $9 \times 3 = 27$

$27 \div 9 = \boxed{3}$

f) $12 \times 2 = 24$

$24 \div 2 = \boxed{12}$

g) $6 \times 4 = 24$

$24 \div 6 = \boxed{4}$

h) $10 \times 3 = 30$

$30 \div 3 = \boxed{10}$

i) $12 \times 4 = 48$

$48 \div 12 = \boxed{4}$

(2) Add these numbers together using mental arithmetic.

✓7 ⊗×2

First seen:
Book 2 Page 2

a) $654 + 37 = \boxed{69\, ?}$ ✗

b) $813 + 49 = \boxed{862}$

c) $216 + 67 = \boxed{283}$

d) $343 + 18 = \boxed{351}$ ✗

e) $437 + 48 = \boxed{485}$

f) $139 + 58 = \boxed{197}$

g) $516 + 36 = \boxed{552}$

h) $178 + 16 = \boxed{194}$

i) $738 + 24 = \boxed{762}$

3 Use written addition to fill in the blanks.   ✓6

First seen: Book 1 Page 70

a)
```
   5  4  3
+     4  6
-----------
   5  8  8
```

b)
```
   7  3  1
+     6  5
-----------
   7  9  6
```

c)
```
   8  2  8
+     5  1
-----------
   8  7  9
```

d)
```
   6  5  2
+     3  5
-----------
   6  8  7
```

e)
```
   9  3  1
+     1  8
-----------
   9  4  9
```

f)
```
   4  2  6
+     4  3
-----------
   4  6  9
```

4 Write the amounts shown.   ✓4

First seen: Book 1 Page 60

a) (£2) (10p) = £ 2 . 10

b) (£1) (50p) (10p) = £ 1 . 60

c) (£1) (20p) (5p) (1p) = £ 1 . 26

d) (£2) (£1) (2p) (2p) (1p) = £ 3 . 05

5 Use the 5 and 10 times tables to fill in the blanks.   ✓6

a) $5 \times 10 = 50$

$50 \div 5 = 10$

b) $12 \times 5 = 60$

$60 \div 12 = 5$

c) $9 \times 10 = 90$

$90 \div 9 = 10$

d) $11 \times 5 = 55$

$55 \div 11 = 5$

e) $4 \times 10 = 40$

$40 \div 10 = 4$

f) $12 \times 10 = 120$

$120 \div 12 = 10$

If this page was a roaring success, try the next one...

6

Exercise 3

Mental arithmetic with bigger numbers

To add or subtract <u>thousands</u>, look at the digit in the <u>thousands column</u>.

$\underline{3}690 + \underline{2}000 = \underline{5}690$ $\underline{9}342 - \underline{4}000 = \underline{5}342$

3000 + 2000 = 5000 ↗   9000 − 4000 = 5000 ↗

Start at **3690** and <u>count up</u> in <u>1000s</u>:

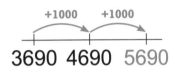

+1000   +1000

3690 4690 5690

Start at **9342** and <u>count down</u> in <u>1000s</u>:

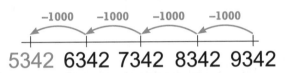

−1000   −1000   −1000   −1000

5342 6342 7342 8342 9342

---

1 Work out each of these using mental arithmetic.   √8

a) 2027 + 2000 = 4027

b) 6871 − 3000 = 3871

c) 8519 + 1000 = 9519

d) 3492 + 5000 = 8492

e) 4907 − 2000 = 2907

f) 5399 − 4000 = 1399

g) 9628 − 7000 = 2628

h) 1662 + 6000 = 7662

2 Tick the boxes next to the true statements.   √6

First seen:
Book 2 Page 4

a) 4 × 3 = 12, so 3 × 12 = 4 ☐

b) 5 × 4 = 20, so 20 ÷ 5 = 4 ✓

c) 9 × 4 = 36, so 36 ÷ 9 = 9 ☐

d) 7 × 5 = 35, so 35 ÷ 5 = 7 ✓

e) 8 × 3 = 24, so 24 × 3 = 8 ☐

f) 6 × 4 = 24, so 24 ÷ 4 = 6 ✓

KS3 Catch-Up Maths — Workbook 2   © CGP — not to be photocopied

3) Subtract these amounts of money.

a) (£1) (20p) (20p) − 10p = £ **1 . 30**

b) (£2) (£2) (£2) (50p) − 40p = £ **6 . 10**

c) (£2) (20p) (5p) (2p) − £1.20 = £ **1 . 07**

d) (£2) (20p) (1p) (1p) − £1.14 = £ **1 . 12** ✗

First seen: Book 1 Page 72

4) Circle the option that makes each sentence correct. ✓6

First seen: Book 1 Page 66

a) 427 rounded to the nearest 100 is: (400) or 500

b) 857 rounded to the nearest 100 is: 800 or (900)

c) 682 rounded to the nearest 100 is: 600 or (700)

d) 715 rounded to the nearest 100 is: (700) or 800

e) 949 rounded to the nearest 100 is: (900) or 1000

f) 555 rounded to the nearest 100 is: 500 or (600)

5) Fill in the missing numbers. ✓6

a) 5464 + 3000 = **8464**   b) 8141 − 7000 = **1141**

c) 6970 − 2000 = **4970**   d) 3291 + 6000 = **9291**

e) 7614 − 4000 = **3614**   f) 1365 + 8000 = **9365**

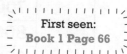

Flip a coin — heads you do the next page, tails you take a break...

Exercise 4

Reading and writing numbers up to 1000

Digits in the <u>hundreds column</u> can be written in <u>words</u> as follows.

Digits	Words
100	one hundred
200	two hundred
300	three hundred
400	four hundred
500	five hundred
600	six hundred
700	seven hundred
800	eight hundred
900	nine hundred

106 = 100 + 6
= one hundred and six

439 = 400 + 39
= four hundred and thirty-nine

740 = 700 + 40
= seven hundred and forty

<u>1000</u> is written as <u>one thousand</u>.

1) Write these numbers in words. ✓4

a) 207   two hundred and seven

b) 459   four hundred and fifty-nine

c) 534   five hundred and thirty-four

d) 961   nine hundred and sixty-one

2) Complete these equations using + or − signs. ✓6

First seen: Book 2 Page 6

a) 5614 − 1000 = 4614

b) 2203 + 3000 = 5203

c) 7239 − 4000 = 3239

d) 8091 − 5000 = 3091

e) 6234 + 3000 = 9234

f) 3487 + 4000 = 7487

3 Use the 2 and 10 times tables to fill in the blanks. ✓9

First seen: Book 2 Page 4

a) 70 ÷ 7 = **10**   b) 16 ÷ 2 = **8**   c) 18 ÷ 9 = **2**

d) 14 ÷ 7 = **2**   e) 8 ÷ 4 = **2**   f) 110 ÷ 10 = **11**

g) 50 ÷ 10 = **5**   h) 12 ÷ 2 = **6**   i) 24 ÷ 12 = **2**

4 Work out these subtractions using mental arithmetic. ✓9

First seen: Book 1 Page 64

a) 700 − 15 = **685**   b) 400 − 43 = **357**   c) 500 − 32 = **468**

d) 900 − 54 = **846**   e) 800 − 29 = **771**   f) 200 − 81 = **119**

g) 500 − 76 = **424**   h) 600 − 68 = **532**   i) 300 − 97 = **203**

5 Write these numbers in digits. ✓6

a) two hundred and forty-two **242**

b) four hundred and seventy-eight **478**

c) three hundred and fifty-seven **357**

d) nine hundred and ninety-five **995**

e) eight hundred and sixty **860**

f) seven hundred and nine **709**

Quick — the Martians are coming! Move on to the next page...

Exercise 5

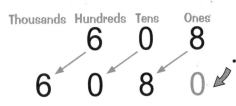

Mental multiplication by 10

When <u>multiplying by 10</u>, move all the digits <u>one place</u> to the <u>left</u>...

Thousands	Hundreds	Tens	Ones
	6	0	8
6	0	8	0

...and fill in the empty place with a <u>zero</u>.

So 608 × 10 = 6080

① **Work out these multiplications using mental arithmetic.** ✓8

a) 361 × 10 = 3610

b) 203 × 10 = 2030

c) 239 × 10 = 2390

d) 189 × 10 = 1890

e) 556 × 10 = 5560

f) 720 × 10 = 7200

g) 824 × 10 = 8240

h) 485 × 10 = 4850

② **Write these numbers in words.** ✓5

First seen:
Book 2 Page 8

a) 421   four hundred and twenty-one

b) 615   six hundred and fifteen

c) 532   five hundred and thirty-two

d) 389   three hundred and eighty-nine

e) 956   nine hundred and fifty-six

3 Use mental arithmetic to add these numbers together. √8 ⊗

First seen:
Book 2 Page 2

a) 452 + 29 = **481**   b) 614 + 68 = **682**   c) 727 + 64 = **781** ⊗

d) 176 + 17 = **193**   e) 838 + 24 = **862**   f) 549 + 35 = **581**

g) 906 + 88 = **994**   h) 337 + 27 = **364**   i) 477 + 18 = **495**

4 Fill in the missing digits. √9

First seen:
Book 1 Page 68

a) 524 − **1** 3 = 511   b) 689 − 7 **6** = 613   c) 4 **7** 9 − 52 = 427

d) 89 **8** − 74 = 824   e) **1** 74 − 43 = 131   f) 784 − **5** 1 = 733

g) 2 **8** 8 − 46 = 242   h) 956 − 2 **4** = 932   i) 3 **7** 9 − 33 = 346

5 Fill in the missing numbers. √6

a) 570 × 10 = **5700**   b) 323 × 10 = **3230**

c) 852 × 10 = **8520**   d) 435 × 10 = **4350**

e) 716 × 10 = **7160**   f) 639 × 10 = **6390**

Time for a rest — you've earned it...

Exercise 6

Mental addition with three-digit and two-digit numbers

Partition the two-digit number into <u>tens</u> and <u>ones</u>. Then add them <u>separately</u>.

$$386 + 45 = ?$$

$45 = \underline{4\ tens} + \underline{5\ ones}$

Add 40...

$$\underline{38}6 + \underline{4}0 = \underline{42}6$$

$\underline{38}$ tens + $\underline{4}$ tens = $\underline{42}$ tens

...then add 5.

$$4\underline{26} + \underline{5} = 4\underline{31}$$

$\underline{26} + \underline{5} = \underline{31}$

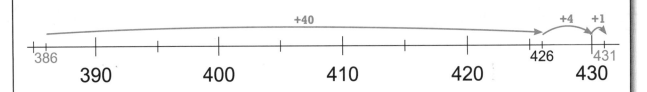

So 386 + 45 = 431

---

(1) **Add these numbers together using mental arithmetic.** ✓5 ⊗

a) 675 + 46 = ~~72~~ ⊗   b) 449 + 94 = 543   c) 786 + 67 = 853

d) 878 + 87 = 965   e) 396 + 49 = 445   f) 174 + 89 = 263

---

(2) **Fill in the missing numbers.**   ✓6

First seen: Book 2 Page 10

a) 404 × 10 = 4040   b) 387 × 10 = 3870

c) 546 × 10 = 5460   d) 285 × 10 = 2850

e) 954 × 10 = 9540   f) 696 × 10 = 6960

---

3 Fill in the blanks.

First seen:
Book 2 Page 6

a) 8138 − 3000 = 5138

b) 5534 + 2000 = 7534

c) 3262 − 1000 = 2262

d) 9291 − 8000 = 1291

e) 6319 + 2000 = 8319

f) 2876 + 5000 = 7876

4 Use written addition to fill in the missing numbers. ✓6

First seen:
Book 1 Page 70

a)
```
    6 2 1
  +   5 2
  -------
    6 7 3
```

b)
```
    4 6 7
  +   2 1
  -------
    4 8 8
```

c)
```
    2 3 4
  +   1 2
  -------
    2 4 6
```

d)
```
    8 5 1
  +   2 1
  -------
    8 7 2
```

e)
```
    5 4 2
  +   5 3
  -------
    5 9 5
```

f)
```
    3 5 3
  +   2 5
  -------
    3 7 8
```

5 Use mental arithmetic to add these numbers. ✓9

a) 482 + 59 = 541

b) 658 + 63 = 721

c) 399 + 62 = 461

d) 565 + 88 = 653

e) 763 + 78 = 841

f) 287 + 37 = 324

g) 183 + 59 = 242

h) 848 + 96 = 944

i) 648 + 83 = 731

...and this little piggy went to the next page and did some more maths.

Exercise 7

To add or subtract <u>hundreds</u>, look at the digits in and above the <u>hundreds</u>.

<u>18</u>40 + <u>3</u>00 = <u>21</u>40   <u>83</u>50 – <u>4</u>00 = <u>79</u>50

<u>18</u> hundreds + <u>3</u> hundreds
= <u>21</u> hundreds

<u>83</u> hundreds – <u>4</u> hundreds
= <u>79</u> hundreds

Count up 200, <u>to 2040</u>,
then another 100, <u>to 2140</u>.

Count down 300, <u>to 8050</u>,
then another 100, <u>to 7950</u>.

```
    +200      +100
 1840 1940 2040 2140
```

```
   -100          -300
 7950 8050 8150 8250 8350
```

① Work out each of these using mental arithmetic.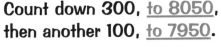

a) 2840 + 300 = 5840 ✗

b) 5630 + 600 = 6230

c) 3267 – 400 = 2867

d) 9654 – 700 = 8954

e) 6153 – 600 = 5553

f) 3621 + 900 = 4321 ✗

② Use mental arithmetic to add these numbers.

First seen:
Book 2 Page 12

a) 584 + 67 = 651

b) 654 + 89 = 743

c) 328 + 95 = 423

d) 458 + 74 = 532

e) 168 + 58 = 226

f) 286 + 38 = 334

3 Write these numbers in words. ✓5

First seen:
Book 2 Page 8

a) 542   five hundred and fourty-two

b) 494   four hundred and nigety-four

c) 640   Six hundred and fourty

d) 857   eight hundred and fifty-seven

e) 205   two hundred and five

4 Use the **3** and **4** times tables to fill in the blanks. ✓9

First seen:
Book 1 Page 50

a) 2 × 3 = 6   b) 7 × 4 = 28   c) 10 × 3 = 30

d) 7 × 3 = 21   e) 4 × 4 = 16   f) 12 × 3 = 36

g) 5 × 4 = 20   h) 9 × 3 = 27   i) 8 × 4 = 32

5 Fill in the missing numbers. ✓5

a) 6923 + 600 = 7523   b) 7218 − 400 = 6818

c) 9507 − 800 = 8707   d) 8826 + 300 = 9126

e) 3843 + 700 = 4543   f) 4694 − 900 = 4064 ⊗

Now switch off and relax before the next Exercise...

16

Exercise 8

Mental subtraction with three-digit and two-digit numbers

Partition the two-digit number into tens and ones,
then subtract them separately.

$$651 - 34 = ?$$

$34 = 3 \text{ tens} + 4 \text{ ones}$

Subtract 30...

$$651 - 30 = 621$$

...then subtract 4.

$$621 - 4 = 617$$

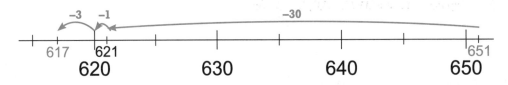

So $651 - 34 = 617$

(1) **Work out each of these using mental arithmetic.** ✓ 6

a) $821 - 17 =$ 804   b) $334 - 28 =$ 306   c) $684 - 69 =$ 615

d) $453 - 24 =$ 429   e) $572 - 35 =$ 537   f) $767 - 58 =$ 709

(2) **Use mental arithmetic to multiply these numbers.** ✓ 6   First seen: Book 2 Page 10

a) $404 \times 10 =$ 4040   b) $387 \times 10 =$ 3870

c) $546 \times 10 =$ 5460   d) $285 \times 10 =$ 2850

e) $954 \times 10 =$ 9540   f) $696 \times 10 =$ 6960

KS3 Catch-Up Maths — Workbook 2

© CGP — not to be photocopied

3 Fill in the missing numbers. ✓5 ✗

First seen: Book 2 Page 14

a) 1560 – 600 = 960

b) 3544 + 700 = 4244

c) 5819 + 400 = 6219

d) 5082 – 500 = 4616 ✗

e) 1982 + 200 = 2182

f) 4956 + 500 = 5456

4 Fill in the blanks with amounts of money. ✓8

First seen: Book 1 Page 72

a) £1.90 – 80p = £ 1.10

b) £7.42 – 20p = £ 7.22

c) £2.50 – £1.10 = £ 1.40

d) £3.56 – £1.30 = £ 2.26

e) £5.81 – 61p = £ 5.20

f) £8.99 – £2.50 = £ 6.49

g) £3.49 – 27p = £ 3.22

h) £6.57 – £3.32 = £ 3.25

5 Subtract these numbers using mental arithmetic. 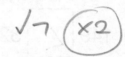 ✓7 ✗2

a) 654 – 25 = 629

b) 465 – 39 = 426

c) 284 – 48 = 216 ✗

d) 566 – 57 = 509

e) 971 – 26 = 944 ✗

f) 155 – 17 = 138

g) 843 – 35 = 808

h) 265 – 36 = 229

i) 454 – 29 = 425

Strut on over to the next page for much more maths...

KS3 Catch-Up Maths — Workbook 2

Exercise 9

Comparing and ordering three-digit numbers

To compare numbers up to 1000, look at the digits in the hundreds column first, then the tens, then the ones. Use the symbols < and >.

$$\underline{}95 < \underline{4}80 \qquad\qquad \underline{6}78 > \underline{4}80$$

No hundreds is less than 4 hundreds.
So 95 is less than 480.

6 hundreds is more than 4 hundreds.
So 678 is greater than 480.

$$4\underline{6}2 < 4\underline{8}0$$

The hundreds digits are the same,
but 6 tens is less than 8 tens.
So 462 is less than 480.

You can then put numbers in size order, e.g. from smallest to largest:

$$95 < 462 < 480 < 678$$

1. Fill in the blanks with either < or >. ✓9

a) 23 < 354   b) 273 > 75   c) 845 > 46

d) 149 < 326   e) 351 > 251   f) 541 < 563

g) 887 > 878   h) 508 > 502   i) 955 < 964

2. Use mental arithmetic for these subtractions. ✓4 ✗2

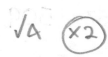
First seen:
Book 2 Page 16

a) 258 − 39 = 219   b) 546 − 28 = 514 ✗   c) 382 − 57 = 325

d) 653 − 15 = 638   e) 487 − 79 = 418 ✗   f) 166 − 37 = 129

3   **Fill in the blanks.**   ✓4 ✗2

First seen: Book 2 Page 14

a) $2134 - 300 = $ 1834

b) $5679 + 500 = $ 6179

c) $7783 - 800 = $ 6983

d) 5239 ✗ $- 400 = 5839$

e) 3216 $+ 600 = 4416$

f) $849 + 500 = $ ~~840~~ ? ✗

---

4   **Use the 3 and 4 times tables to fill in the blanks.**   ✓6

First seen: Book 2 Page 4

a) $7 \times 3 = 21$

$21 \div 3 = $ 7

b) $12 \times 4 = 48$

$48 \div 12 = $ 4

c) $9 \times 3 = 27$

$27 \div 3 = $ 9

d) $11 \times 4 = 44$

$44 \div 11 = $ 4

e) $2 \times 3 = 6$

$6 \div 3 = $ 2

f) $7 \times 4 = 28$

$28 \div 7 = $ 4

---

5   **Put these numbers in order from smallest to largest.**   ✓6

a) 600, 500, 400:   400, 500, 600

b) 130, 95, 350:   95, 130, 350

c) 870, 843, 865:   843, 865, 870

d) 634, 638, 637:   634, 637, 638

e) 752, 863, 611:   611, 752, 863

f) 831, 587, 448:   448, 587, 831

Time for a breather before the next page, I reckon...

Exercise 10

Mental subtraction with three-digit and two-digit numbers

Partition the two-digit number into tens and ones, then subtract them separately.

$$321 - 45 = ?$$

$$45 = \underline{4 \text{ tens}} + \underline{5 \text{ ones}}$$

Subtract 40...

$$321 - 40 = 281$$

$$\underline{32} \text{ tens} - \underline{4} \text{ tens} = \underline{28} \text{ tens}$$

...then subtract 5.

$$281 - 5 = 276$$

$$\underline{81} - \underline{5} = \underline{76}$$

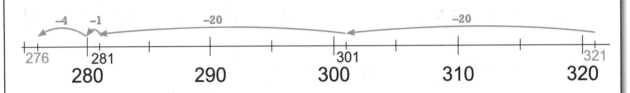

$$\text{So } 321 - 45 = 276$$

(1) Subtract these numbers using mental arithmetic. ✓6

a) $452 - 64 =$ 388   b) $541 - 76 =$ 465   c) $253 - 87 =$ 166

d) $614 - 55 =$ 559   e) $337 - 48 =$ 289   f) $752 - 94 =$ 658

(2) Write true or false for each of these comparisons. ✓6

First seen: Book 2 Page 18

a) $458 > 448$ True   b) $663 < 450$ False

c) $323 < 332$ True   d) $954 > 862$ True

e) $853 > 891$ False   f) $785 > 872$ False

3 Use mental arithmetic to add these numbers. ✓9

First seen: Book 2 Page 12

a) 483 + 49 = 542 ⊗   b) 365 + 76 = 441   c) 854 + 68 = 922

d) 554 + 97 = 651   e) 769 + 54 = 823   f) 336 + 86 = 422

g) 678 + 45 = 723   h) 496 + 67 = 563   i) 298 + 94 = 392

4 Fill in the missing numbers to add the amounts of money. ✓8

First seen: Book 1 Page 60

a) £3.40 + 10p = £ 3 . 50   b) £8.21 + £1.01 = £ 9 . 22

c) £1.70 + 24p = £ 1 . 94   d) £5.60 + £3.20 = £ 8 . 80

e) £4.20 + £1.11 = £ 5 . 31   f) £2.63 + £1.30 = £ 3 . 93

g) £7.18 + 51p = £ 7 . 69   h) £5.14 + £2.62 = £ 7 . 76

5 Work these out using mental arithmetic. ✓7 ⊗

a) 514 − 56 = 458   b) 651 − 66 = 585   c) 743 − 74 = 669

d) 684 − 95 = 589   e) 221 − 48 = 173   f) 643 − 57 = 586

g) 451 − 76 = 375   h) 542 − 88 = 453 ⊗

As if by magic, there are more questions on the next page...

Exercise 11

The 6 and 9 times tables

Learn the 6 and 9 times tables until you can recall them without looking.

1 × 6 = 6	5 × 6 = 30	1 × 9 = 9
2 × 6 = 12	So: 30 ÷ 5 = 6	2 × 9 = 18
3 × 6 = 18	30 ÷ 6 = 5	3 × 9 = 27
4 × 6 = 24		4 × 9 = 36
5 × 6 = 30		5 × 9 = 45
6 × 6 = 36		6 × 9 = 54
7 × 6 = 42		7 × 9 = 63
8 × 6 = 48		8 × 9 = 72
9 × 6 = 54		9 × 9 = 81
10 × 6 = 60		10 × 9 = 90
11 × 6 = 66		11 × 9 = 99
12 × 6 = 72		12 × 9 = 108

30 divides into 6 groups of 5 and 5 groups of 6.

1 Fill in the missing numbers from the 6 and 9 times tables. √9

a) 6 × 9 = 54   b) 4 × 6 = 24   c) 10 × 9 = 90

d) 6 × 6 = 36   e) 7 × 9 = 63   f) 5 × 6 = 30

g) 12 × 6 = 72   h) 8 × 9 = 72   i) 7 × 6 = 42

2 Round these numbers to the nearest 100. √9

First seen:
Book 1 Page 66

a) 775 800   b) 261 300   c) 618 600

d) 901 900   e) 676 700   f) 824 800

g) 138 100   h) 481 500   i) 353 400

3 Use mental arithmetic for these subtractions. ✓9

First seen:
Book 2 Page 20

a) 852 – 73 = 779   b) 631 – 65 = 566   c) 218 – 29 = 189

d) 564 – 87 = 477   e) 463 – 76 = 387   f) 742 – 66 = 676

g) 333 – 54 = 279   h) 827 – 49 = 778   i) 474 – 88 = 386

4 Fill in the missing numbers. ✓6

First seen:
Book 2 Page 6

a) 4321 + 2000 = 6321   b) 2773 – 1000 = 1773

c) 5814 + 3000 = 8814   d) 8640 – 7000 = 1640

e) 9281 – 2000 = 7281   f) 3519 + 5000 = 8519

5 Use the 6 and 9 times tables to fill in the blanks. ✓9

a) 2 × 9 = 18   b) 10 × 6 = 60   c) 9 × 9 = 81

   18 ÷ 2 = 9   60 ÷ 10 = 6   81 ÷ 9 = 9

d) 11 × 6 = 66   e) 4 × 9 = 36   f) 12 × 9 = 108

   66 ÷ 6 = 11   36 ÷ 9 = 4   108 ÷ 9 = 12

g) 11 × 9 = 99   h) 8 × 6 = 48   i) 3 × 9 = 27

   99 ÷ 11 = 9   48 ÷ 6 = 8   27 ÷ 9 = 3

On to the next Exercise — watch your step...

KS3 Catch-Up Maths — Workbook 2

Exercise 12

Write one number on top of the other, <u>lining up</u> the columns.
Add the digits in the <u>ones column</u>, then the tens, then the hundreds.
If the total of a column is <u>10</u> or more, carry <u>1</u> to the <u>next column</u> to the <u>left</u>.

Hundreds Tens Ones

$$6\ 1\ 3$$
$$+\ \ \ 3\ 9$$
$$\overline{6\ 5\ 2}$$

$3 + 9 = 12$, so write the $\underline{2}$ here...

$1 + 3 + 1 = 5$ ...and carry $\underline{1}$ to add to the next column left.

Hundreds Tens Ones

$$1\ 7\ 5$$
$$+\ \ \ 3\ 2$$
$$\overline{2\ 0\ 7}$$

$7 + 3 = 10$, so write the $\underline{0}$ here... ...and carry $\underline{1}$ to add to the next column left.

$613 + 39 = 652$ $175 + 32 = 207$

1 Use written addition to add these numbers together. ✓6

a)
$$6\ 3\ 4$$
$$+\ \ \ 2\ 8$$
$$\overline{6\ 6\ 2}$$

b)
$$1\ 5\ 5$$
$$+\ \ \ 3\ 6$$
$$\overline{1\ 9\ 1}$$

c)
$$4\ 5\ 4$$
$$+\ \ \ 1\ 9$$
$$\overline{4\ 7\ 3}$$

d)
$$5\ 7\ 1$$
$$+\ \ \ 5\ 8$$
$$\overline{6\ 2\ 9}$$

e)
$$3\ 2\ 6$$
$$+\ \ \ 9\ 1$$
$$\overline{4\ 1\ 7}$$

f)
$$8\ 4\ 1$$
$$+\ \ \ 8\ 5$$
$$\overline{9\ 2\ 6}$$

2 Fill in the missing numbers from the 6 and 9 times tables. ✓9

First seen: Book 2 Page 22

a) $3 \times 9 = 27$

b) $8 \times 6 = 48$

c) $12 \times 9 = 108$

d) $10 \times 6 = 60$

e) $5 \times 9 = 45$

f) $11 \times 6 = 66$

g) $9 \times 9 = 81$

h) $11 \times 9 = 99$

i) $4 \times 9 = 36$

3 Fill in the missing amounts of money. ✓6

First seen: Book 1 Page 72

a) £5.40 – 40 p = £5.00   b) £8.20 – £ 1 . 10 = £7.10

c) £3.83 – 50 p = £3.33   d) £4.90 – £ 2 . 50 = £2.40

e) £6.50 – £ 6 . 00 = 50p   f) £7.81 – £ 1 . 60 = £6.21

 4 Write these numbers in digits. ✓5

First seen: Book 2 Page 8

a) nine hundred and ninety-eight   998

b) six hundred and seventeen   617

c) five hundred and fifty   550

d) three hundred and seven   307

e) one thousand   1000

5 Add these numbers together using written addition. ✓6

a)
```
   1 7 9
 +   1 5
 -------
   1 9 4
```

b)
```
   7 5 4
 +   6 3
 -------
   8 1 7
```

c)
```
   5 6 8
 +   2 9
 -------
   5 9 7
```

d)
```
   4 8 3
 +   7 2
 -------
   5 5 5
```

e)
```
   3 6 5
 +   8 4
 -------
   4 4 9
```

f)
```
   7 6 6
 +   1 4
 -------
   7 8 0
```

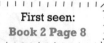

Don't take on too much at once — have a break...

Exercise 13

The 7 and 8 times tables

Learn the <u>7 and 8 times tables</u> until you can <u>recall</u> them without looking.

1 × 7 = 7		1 × 8 = 8
2 × 7 = 14		2 × 8 = 16
3 × 7 = 21	6 × 7 = 42	3 × 8 = 24
4 × 7 = 28	So: 42 ÷ 6 = 7	4 × 8 = 32
5 × 7 = 35	42 ÷ 7 = 6	5 × 8 = 40
6 × 7 = 42		6 × 8 = 48
7 × 7 = 49		7 × 8 = 56
8 × 7 = 56	9 × 8 = 72	8 × 8 = 64
9 × 7 = 63	So: 72 ÷ 9 = 8	9 × 8 = 72
10 × 7 = 70	72 ÷ 8 = 9	10 × 8 = 80
11 × 7 = 77		11 × 8 = 88
12 × 7 = 84		12 × 8 = 96

1 Fill in the missing numbers from the 7 and 8 times tables. ✓9

a) 5 × 7 = 35   b) 2 × 8 = 16   c) 10 × 7 = 70

d) 4 × 8 = 32   e) 7 × 7 = 49   f) 6 × 8 = 48

g) 11 × 7 = 77   h) 8 × 8 = 64   i) 12 × 7 = 84

2 Use written addition to add these numbers together. ✓6

First seen: Book 2 Page 24

a)
```
  1 4 5
+   3 6
-------
  1 8 1
```

b)
```
  2 2 7
+   4 4
-------
  2 7 1
```

c)
```
  5 6 8
+   2 3
-------
  5 9 1
```

d)
```
  6 6 7
+   1 8
-------
  6 8 5
```

e)
```
  3 3 3
+   4 7
-------
  3 8 0
```

f)
```
  9 0 8
+   6 6
-------
  9 7 4
```

3 Put these numbers in order from smallest to largest. ✓4

First seen:
Book 2 Page 18

a) 345, 246, 598, 426: 246 , 345 , 426 , 598

b) 675, 431, 896, 513: 431 , 513 , 675 , 896

c) 289, 605, 168, 608: 168 , 289 , 605 , 608

d) 123, 356, 569, 144: 123 , 144 , 356 , 569

4 Multiply these numbers using mental arithmetic. ✓6

First seen:
Book 2 Page 10

a) 645 × 10 = 6456

b) 216 × 10 = 2160

c) 478 × 10 = 4780

d) 908 × 10 = 9080

e) 737 × 10 = 7370

f) 623 × 10 = 6230

5 Use the 7 and 8 times tables to fill in the blanks. ✓9

a) 3 × 7 = 21   b) 8 × 2 = 16   c) 4 × 7 = 28

d) 9 × 8 = 72   e) 7 × 10 = 70   f) 6 × 8 = 48

g) 8 × 7 = 56   h) 3 × 8 = 24   i) 12 × 7 = 84

Press on to the next page...

Exercise 14

Rounding four-digit numbers to the nearest 10

To round to the <u>nearest ten</u>, look at the digit in the <u>ones</u> column.
If it's <u>less than 5</u>, round <u>down</u>, leaving the number of tens <u>as it is</u>.
If it's <u>5 or more</u>, round <u>up</u> to the next ten.

Th H T O
5 7 6 <u>2</u> ⟶ 5 7 <u>6 0</u>

Th H T O
1 2 7 <u>5</u> ⟶ 1 2 <u>8 0</u>

There are <u>2 ones</u>,
so round <u>down</u> to **5760**.

There are <u>5 ones</u>,
so round <u>up</u> to **1280**.

---

1 Circle the option that makes each sentence correct. ✓5

a) 8765 rounded to the nearest 10 is: 8760 or (8770)

b) 1928 rounded to the nearest 10 is: 1920 or (1930)

c) 3673 rounded to the nearest 10 is: (3670) or 3680

d) 2862 rounded to the nearest 10 is: (2860) or 2870

e) 6544 rounded to the nearest 10 is: (6540) or 6550

2 Use the 7 and 8 times tables to fill in the blanks. ✓9

First seen:
Book 2 Page 26

a) $88 \div 8 = 11$ b) $64 \div 8 = 8$ c) $28 \div 7 = 4$

d) $96 \div 8 = 12$ e) $77 \div 11 = 7$ f) $80 \div 8 = 10$

g) $63 \div 7 = 9$ h) $24 \div 8 = 3$ i) $35 \div 7 = 5$

3 Work out each of these using mental arithmetic. ✓6

First seen:
Book 2 Page 14

a) 720 + 400 = 1120

b) 8740 + 600 = 9340

c) 1896 − 900 = 896

d) 4239 − 700 = 3539

e) 2230 − 500 = 1730

f) 834 + 300 = 1134

4 Fill in the missing numbers. ✓9

First seen:
Book 2 Page 12

a) 389 + 42 = 431

b) 213 + 96 = 309

c) 456 + 87 = 543

d) 598 + 26 = 624

e) 965 + 54 = 1019

f) 153 + 68 = 221

g) 790 + 69 = 859

h) 823 + 87 = 910

i) 690 + 25 = 715

5 Round each number to the nearest ten. ✓9

a) 1267: 1270

b) 9872: 9870

c) 3245: 3250

d) 8721: 8720

e) 4091: 4090

f) 7132: 7130

g) 5956: 5960

h) 2685: 2690

i) 1402: 1400

Keep working hard and you'll be on track for success...

Exercise 15

Written addition with three-digit and two-digit numbers

When doing written addition, add each column, working from right to left. If the total of a column is <u>10</u> or more, carry the <u>tens</u> to the <u>next column</u> to the <u>left</u>. Sometimes you will need to do this <u>more than once</u>.

$$385 + 47 = ?$$

Hundreds	Tens	Ones
3	8	5
+	4	7
		2

₁

5 + 7 = 12
...so 1 is added to the tens.

Hundreds	Tens	Ones
3	8	5
+	4	7
	3	2

_{1 1}

8 + 4 + 1 = 13
...so 1 is added to the hundreds.

Hundreds	Tens	Ones
3	8	5
+	4	7
4	3	2

_{1 1}

3 + 1 = 4

$$385 + 47 = 432$$

---

(1) Use written addition to add these numbers together. ✓6

a)
```
  8 7 2
+   3 9
-------
  9 1 1
```

b)
```
  3 6 5
+   5 6
-------
  4 2 1
```

c)
```
  5 8 9
+   6 3
-------
  6 5 2
```

d)
```
  1 4 5
+   9 8
-------
  2 4 3
```

e)
```
  2 6 5
+   7 9
-------
  3 4 4
```

f)
```
  6 4 9
+   6 9
-------
  7 1 8
```

---

(2) Round each number to the nearest ten. ✓6

First seen: Book 2 Page 28

a) 9844: `9840`   b) 1569: `1570`   c) 8231: `8230`

d) 2306: `2300`   e) 7212: `7210`   f) 3923: `3920`

---

3   **Use mental arithmetic to subtract these numbers.** ✓9   First seen: Book 2 Page 16

a) 123 – 14 = 109   b) 568 – 49 = 519   c) 285 – 59 = 226

d) 864 – 26 = 838   e) 377 – 68 = 309   f) 432 – 23 = 409

g) 965 – 57 = 908   h) 661 – 34 = 627   i) 736 – 18 = 718

4   **Use the 6 and 9 times tables to fill in the blanks.** ✓9   First seen: Book 2 Page 22

a) 18 ÷ 3 = 6   b) 90 ÷ 10 = 9   c) 66 ÷ 6 = 11

d) 18 ÷ 2 = 9   e) 24 ÷ 6 = 4   f) 45 ÷ 9 = 5

g) 54 ÷ 6 = 9   h) 72 ÷ 9 = 8   i) 72 ÷ 6 = 12

5   **Add these numbers together using written addition.** ✓6

a) 126 + 85 = 211   b) 345 + 77 = 422   c) 482 + 39 = 521

d) 555 + 88 = 643   e) 237 + 64 = 301   f) 688 + 32 = 720

Here's the key to unlocking the next page of questions...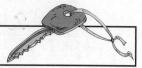

Exercise 16

Mental subtraction with three-digit numbers

To subtract a three-digit number, <u>partition</u> it into <u>hundreds</u>, <u>tens</u> and <u>ones</u>. Subtract the hundreds, the tens and the ones <u>separately</u>.

<u>5</u>00 – 346 = ?   346 = <u>3 hundreds</u> + <u>4 tens</u> + <u>6 ones</u>

<u>5</u>00 – <u>3</u>00 = <u>2</u>00   Subtract the <u>3 hundreds</u>...

<u>2</u>00 – <u>4</u>0 = <u>16</u>0   ...then the <u>4 tens</u>...

1<u>6</u>0 – <u>6</u> = <u>15</u>4   ...then the <u>6 ones</u>.

(1) Subtract these numbers using mental arithmetic. ✓7 ⊗

a) 900 – 486 = 414

b) 200 – 159 = 41

c) 800 – 222 = 688 ⊗

d) 400 – 387 = 13

e) 600 – 597 = 03

f) 700 – 666 = 34

g) 200 – 160 = 40

h) 500 – 203 = 297

(2) Use written addition to add these numbers together. ✓6

First seen: Book 2 Page 30

a)
```
  6 5 4
+   6 7
-------
  7 2 1
```

b)
```
  3 4 5
+   7 5
-------
  4 2 0
```

c)
```
  4 5 1
+   8 9
-------
  5 4 0
```

d)
```
  1 8 5
+   3 6
-------
  2 2 1
```

e)
```
  2 5 4
+   6 8
-------
  3 2 2
```

f)
```
  6 4 8
+   6 6
-------
  7 1 4
```

3 Fill in the missing numbers from the 7 and 8 times tables. ✓9

First seen:
Book 2 Page 26

a) 9 × 8 = 72

b) 56 ÷ 7 = 8

c) 11 × 8 = 88

d) 5 × 7 = 35

e) 3 × 8 = 24

f) 70 ÷ 7 = 10

g) 72 ÷ 8 = 9

h) 6 × 7 = 42

i) 10 × 8 = 80

4 Put these numbers in order from largest to smallest. ✓4

First seen:
Book 2 Page 18

a) 235, 156, 567, 444: 567 , 444 , 235 , 156

b) 987, 886, 887, 986: 987 , 986 , 887 , 886

c) 321, 589, 432, 634: 634 , 589 , 432 , 321

d) 756, 586, 568, 865: 865 , 756 , 586 , 568

5 Fill in the blanks. ✓5 ⊗

a) 200 − 176 = 24

b) 500 − 364 = 236 ⊗

c) 900 − 706 = 194

d) 300 − 279 = 21

e) 600 − 497 = 103

f) 800 − 624 = 176

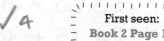

Shimmy on over to the next page for lots more questions...

Exercise 17

Adding money

To <u>add</u> amounts of money:
1) Split one amount into <u>pounds</u> (£) and <u>pence</u> (p). **£1 = 100p.**
   It could help to <u>partition</u> the pence into <u>tens</u> and <u>ones</u>.
2) Add on the <u>pounds</u> first, then the <u>pence</u>.

$$£1.75 + £2.43 \leftarrow £2 + 40p + 3p$$

£1.75 + £2 = £3.75
£3.75 + 40p = £4.15
£4.15 + 3p = £4.18

+£2   +40p +3p
£1.75   £3.75 £4.15
£2   £3   £4 £4.18

£1.75 + £2.43 = £4.18

---

(1) Add these amounts of money.   ✓ ⚹8

a) £1.23 + £4.90:   £4.90 = £4 + 90p,   £1.23 + £4 = £ `5 . 23`

£ `5 . 23` + 90p = £ `6 . 13`

b) £2.45 + £5.62:   £5.62 = £5 + 62p,   £2.45 + £5 = £ `7 . 45`

£ `7 . 45` + 62p = £ `8 . 07`

c) £7.35 + £2.46:   £2.46 = £2 + 46p,   £7.35 + £2 = £ `9 . 35`

£ `9 . 35` + 46p = £ `9 . 81`

(2) Use mental arithmetic to subtract these numbers.   √3 ⊗

First seen: Book 2 Page 32

a) 700 – 169 = `6 31` ⊗   b) 300 – 246 = `54`

c) 400 – 367 = `33`   d) 600 – 498 = `102`

3 Round each number to the nearest ten. √6

First seen: Book 2 Page 28

a) 3456: 3460   b) 8903: 8900   c) 7659: 7660

d) 1735: 1340 (circled, corrected)   e) 1248: 1250   f) 6752: 6750

4 Use written addition to add these numbers together. √6

First seen: Book 2 Page 24

a)
```
  1 2 3
+   4 9
-------
  1 7 2
```
b)
```
  3 6 4
+   5 2
-------
  4 1 6
```
c)
```
  6 8 6
+   3 1
-------
  7 1 7
```
d)
```
  5 4 8
+   7 1
-------
  6 1 9
```
e)
```
  4 4 4
+   7 4
-------
  5 1 8
```
f)
```
  9 2 3
+   1 8
-------
  9 4 1
```

5 Add these amounts of money. √8

a) £3.54 + £4.49:   £4.49 = £4 + 49p,   £3.54 + £4 = £7.54

£7.54 + 49p = £8.03

b) £2.21 + £6.89:   £6.89 = £6 + 89p,   £2.21 + £6 = £8.21

£8.21 + 89p = £9.10

c) £2.67 + £1.36:   £1.36 = £1 + 36p,   £2.67 + £1 = £3.67

£3.67 + 36p = £4.03

Stay strong and keep working through these exercises...

Exercise 18

Written addition with three-digit numbers

Write one number on top of the other, <u>lining up</u> the columns.
Add the digits in the <u>ones column</u>, then the <u>tens</u>, then the <u>hundreds</u>.
If the total of a column is <u>10</u> or more, add 1 to the <u>next column</u> on the <u>left</u>.

Hundreds Tens Ones

```
  3 6 8
+ 4 1 5
―――――
  7 8 3
    1
```

$8 + 5 = 13$,
so write the
<u>3</u> here...

$6 + 1 + 1 = 8$ ...and add <u>1</u> to the next column left.

Hundreds Tens Ones

```
  2 5 8
+ 6 7 1
―――――
  9 2 9
  1
```

$5 + 7 = 12$,
so write the
<u>2</u> here...

...and add <u>1</u> to the
next column left.

$368 + 415 = 783$ $258 + 671 = 929$

✓6

1 Use written addition to add these numbers together.

a)
```
  3 6 8
+ 4 1 5
―――――
  7 8 3
```

b)
```
  2 2 7
+ 6 6 4
―――――
  8 9 1
```

c)
```
  6 3 0
+ 2 8 4
―――――
  9 1 4
```

d)
```
  3 4 1
+ 2 7 5
―――――
  6 1 6
```

e)
```
  8 0 6
+ 1 7 5
―――――
  9 8 1
```

f)
```
  2 3 7
+ 2 4 5
―――――
  4 8 2
```

2 Add these amounts of money.

✓5 ⊗

First seen: Book 2 Page 34

a) £3.45 + £2.72:   £2.72 = £2 + 72p,   £3.45 + £2 = £ 5 . 45

£ 5 . 45 + 72p = £ 6 . 29 ⊗  £6.17

b) £2.86 + £1.15:   £1.15 = £1 + 15p,   £2.86 + £1 = £ 3 . 86

£ 3 . 86 + 15p = £ 4 . 0 1

3 Use your knowledge of the times tables to fill in the blanks.

First seen:
Book 2 Page 4

a) 12 ÷ 3 = 4   b) 25 ÷ 5 = 5   c) 24 ÷ 2 = 12

d) 40 ÷ 10 = 4   e) 110 ÷ 10 = 11   f) 30 ÷ 5 = 6

g) 24 ÷ 6 = 4   h) 40 ÷ 5 = 8   i) 30 ÷ 10 = 3

4 Use mental arithmetic to subtract these numbers.

First seen:
Book 2 Page 20

a) 321 – 43 = 288   b) 478 – 86 = 392   c) 590 – 92 = 498

d) 755 – 62 = 693   e) 825 – 34 = 791   f) 961 – 83 = 878

g) 485 – 91 = 394   h) 238 – 54 = 184   i) 618 – 26 = 592

5 Add these numbers together using written addition.

a) 5 4 7
  + 4 2 9
    9 7 6

b) 2 6 3
  + 3 5 1
    6 1 4

c) 6 4 1
  + 2 7 2
    8 1 3

d) 4 8 8
  + 2 3 1
    7 1 9

e) 2 3 7
  + 4 1 4
    6 5 1

f) 6 0 2
  + 3 1 9
    9 2 1

Sing a happy song — you're halfway there...

KS3 Catch-Up Maths — Workbook 2

Exercise 19

Learn the 11 and 12 times tables until you can recall them without looking.

$1 \times 11 = 11$	$1 \times 12 = 12$
$2 \times 11 = 22$	$2 \times 12 = 24$
$3 \times 11 = 33$	$3 \times 12 = 36$
$4 \times 11 = 44$	$4 \times 12 = 48$
$5 \times 11 = 55$	$5 \times 12 = 60$
$6 \times 11 = 66$	$6 \times 12 = 72$
$7 \times 11 = 77$	$7 \times 12 = 84$
$8 \times 11 = 88$	$8 \times 12 = 96$
$9 \times 11 = 99$	$9 \times 12 = 108$
$10 \times 11 = 110$	$10 \times 12 = 120$
$11 \times 11 = 121$	$11 \times 12 = 132$
$12 \times 11 = 132$	$12 \times 12 = 144$

$7 \times 11 = 77$
So: $77 \div 7 = 11$
$77 \div 11 = 7$

$8 \times 12 = 96$
So: $96 \div 8 = 12$
$96 \div 12 = 8$

---

1 Fill in the missing numbers from the 11 and 12 times tables. ✓6

a) $5 \times 12 =$ ⟦60⟧

b) $3 \times 11 =$ ⟦33⟧

c) $11 \times 12 =$ ⟦132⟧

d) $8 \times 11 =$ ⟦88⟧

e) $7 \times 12 =$ ⟦84⟧

f) $9 \times 12 =$ ⟦108⟧

---

2 Use written addition to add these numbers together. ✓6

First seen:
Book 2 Page 36

a)
```
    5  1  5
 +  1  5  6
 ----------
    6  7  1
```

b)
```
    2  5  8
 +  4  3  4
 ----------
    6  9  2
```

c)
```
    6  6  5
 +  2  7  3
 ----------
    9  3  8
```

d)
```
    1  4  7
 +  6  2  4
 ----------
    7  7  1
```

e)
```
    6  2  4
 +  2  9  2
 ----------
    9  1  6
```

f)
```
    2  6  2
 +  3  9  3
 ----------
    6  5  5
```

KS3 Catch-Up Maths — Workbook 2

(3) Use mental arithmetic to do these subtractions. ✓8

First seen:
Book 2 Page 32

a) 500 − 325 = **175** ✓

b) 300 − 121 = **179**

c) 800 − 487 = **313** ✓

d) 400 − 276 = **124**

e) 700 − 594 = **106** ✓

f) 900 − 682 = **218**

g) 800 − 318 = **482**

h) 600 − 363 = **237**

(4) Fill in the missing numbers. ✓6

First seen:
Book 2 Page 22

a) 6 × 9 = **54**

b) **3** × 6 = 18

c) 11 × **9** = 99

d) **8** × 6 = 48

e) 7 × **6** = 42

f) **12** × 9 = 108

(5) Use the 11 and 12 times tables to fill in the missing numbers. ✓9

a) 4 × 11 = 44

44 ÷ 4 = **11**

b) 9 × 11 = 99

99 ÷ 9 = **11**

c) 6 × 12 = 72

72 ÷ 12 = **6**

d) 2 × 11 = 22

22 ÷ 11 = **2**

e) 7 × 12 = 84

84 ÷ 7 = **12**

f) 10 × 11 = 110

110 ÷ 10 = **11**

g) 8 × 12 = 96

96 ÷ **12** = 8

h) 12 × 12 = 144

144 ÷ **12** = 12

i) 5 × 11 = 55

55 ÷ 11 = 5

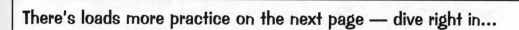

There's loads more practice on the next page — dive right in...

Exercise 20

Mental addition with three-digit numbers

Partition one number into <u>hundreds</u> and <u>tens</u>. Then add them <u>separately</u>.

$$450 + 230 = \text{?}$$

230 = <u>2 hundreds</u> + <u>3 tens</u>

$$4\underline{5}0 + \underline{2}00 = 6\underline{5}0 \qquad 6\underline{5}0 + \underline{3}0 = 6\underline{8}0$$

Add the <u>2 hundreds</u>...   ...then the <u>3 tens</u>.

---

(1) Add these numbers together using mental arithmetic.   ✓/10

a) 760 + 120 = $\boxed{880}$

b) 430 + 540 = $\boxed{970}$

c) 360 + 330 = $\boxed{690}$

d) 510 + 260 = $\boxed{970}$

e) 650 + 240 = $\boxed{890}$

f) 190 + 720 = $\boxed{910}$

g) 470 + 350 = $\boxed{820}$

h) 180 + 540 = $\boxed{720}$

i) 670 + 160 = $\boxed{830}$

j) 580 + 380 = $\boxed{960}$

---

(2) Fill in the missing numbers from the 11 and 12 times tables.   ✓/6

First seen: Book 2 Page 38

a) 6 × 11 = $\boxed{66}$

b) 4 × 12 = $\boxed{48}$

c) 10 × 12 = $\boxed{120}$

d) 7 × 11 = $\boxed{77}$

e) 3 × 11 = $\boxed{33}$

f) 8 × 12 = $\boxed{96}$

---

3 Fill in the blanks to add these amounts of money. ✓5 ⊗

First seen: Book 2 Page 34

a) £5.50 + 60p = £ 6 . 10

b) £3.40 + £4.80 = £ 8 . 20

c) £7.93 + 59p = £ 8̶ ⑨ . 5 2 ⊗

d) £2.51 + £7.80 = £ 10 . 31

e) £1.26 + 85p = £ 2 . 11

f) £4.46 + £2.55 = £ 7 . 01

4 Write these numbers in words. ✓5

First seen: Book 2 Page 8

a) 318 — Three hundred and eighteen.

b) 142 — One hundred and fourty-two

c) 258 — two hundred and fifty-eight.

d) 394 — three hundred and ninety-four

e) 627 — Six hundred and twenty-seven.

5 Use mental arithmetic to do these additions. ✓6

a) 420 + 420 = 840

b) 240 + 550 = 790

c) 110 + 660 = 770

d) 680 + 230 = 910

e) 390 + 470 = 860

f) 370 + 580 = 950

Gone fishin', catch you later...

Exercise 21

1 Fill in the blanks to do these subtractions with money. ✓6

a) £3.40 – £1.50:   £1.50 = £1 + 50p,   £3.40 – £1 = £ 2 . 40

£ 2 . 40 – 50p = £ 1 . 90

b) £6.13 – £2.60:   £2.60 = £2 + 60p,   £6.13 – £2 = £ 4 . 13

£ 4 . 13 – 60p = £ 3 . 53

2 Use mental arithmetic to add these numbers. ✓6

First seen:
Book 2 Page 40

a) 540 + 230 = 770   b) 780 + 120 = 900

c) 210 + 530 = 740   d) 160 + 660 = 820

e) 170 + 340 = 510   f) 690 + 230 = 920

(3) Add these numbers together using written addition. ✓9

First seen: Book 2 Page 36

a)
```
  ⁶6  5  2
+ 2  6  0
─────────
  9  1  2
```

b)
```
  5  ⁴4  9
+ 3   1  8
──────────
  8   6  7
```

c)
```
  ¹2  2  1
+ 4  9  3
─────────
  7  1  4
```

d)
```
  3  ²2  6
+ 4   6  5
──────────
  7   9  1
```

e)
```
  6  ²2  ¹7
+ 1   5   4
───────────
  7   8   1
```

f)
```
  ¹2  8  4
+ 5   6  2
──────────
  8   4  6
```

g)
```
  5  ¹1  7
+ 3   4  5
──────────
  8   6  2
```

h)
```
  ¹7  7  2
+ 1   6  7
──────────
  9   3  9
```

i)
```
  ¹4  7  3
+ 3   8  5
──────────
  8   5  8
```

(4) Use the 7 and 8 times tables to fill in the missing numbers. ✓6

First seen: Book 2 Page 26

a) $49 \div 7 = $ 7

b) $96 \div 8 = $ 12

c) $63 \div 9 = $ 7

d) $88 \div 11 = $ 8

e) $28 \div 4 = $ 7

f) $56 \div 7 = $ 8

(5) Fill in the blanks with amounts of money. ✓2 ⊗4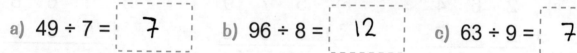

a) £1.20 − 75p = £ 1 . 95 ⊗

b) £6.11 − £4.20 = £ 2 . 91 ⊗

c) £9.08 − 63p = £ 8 . 45

d) £4.29 − £1.33 = £ 3 . 96 ⊗

e) £6.52 − 80p = £ 5 . 72

f) £7.66 − £4.72 = £ 3 . 94 ⊗

Keep up the good pace and head on to the next Exercise...

Exercise 22

Written addition with three-digit numbers

Write one number on top of the other, <u>lining up</u> the columns.
Add the digits in the <u>ones column</u>, then the <u>tens</u>, then the <u>hundreds</u>.
If the total of a column is <u>10</u> or more, add <u>1</u> to the <u>next column</u> to the <u>left</u>.
Sometimes you will need to do this <u>more than once</u>.

Hundreds Tens Ones

$$
\begin{array}{r}
3\ 5\ 8 \\
+\ 4\ 6\ 9 \\
\hline
7 \\
\end{array}
$$
1

8 + 9 = 17, so write the <u>7</u> here...

...and add <u>1</u> to the next column to the left.

Hundreds Tens Ones

$$
\begin{array}{r}
3\ 5\ 8 \\
+\ 4\ 6\ 9 \\
\hline
8\ 2\ 7 \\
\end{array}
$$
1 1

5 + 6 + 1 = 12, so write the <u>2</u> here...

...and add <u>1</u> to the next column to the left.
3 + 4 + 1 = 8

So 358 + 469 = 827

1 Use written addition to add these numbers together.

a)
$$
\begin{array}{r}
2\ 6\ 4 \\
+\ 2\ 6\ 7 \\
\hline
\end{array}
$$

b)
$$
\begin{array}{r}
5\ 7\ 9 \\
+\ 3\ 5\ 2 \\
\hline
\end{array}
$$

c)
$$
\begin{array}{r}
1\ 6\ 8 \\
+\ 6\ 5\ 5 \\
\hline
\end{array}
$$

d)
$$
\begin{array}{r}
6\ 4\ 9 \\
+\ 2\ 8\ 8 \\
\hline
\end{array}
$$

e)
$$
\begin{array}{r}
2\ 4\ 5 \\
+\ 5\ 6\ 8 \\
\hline
\end{array}
$$

f)
$$
\begin{array}{r}
5\ 9\ 4 \\
+\ 1\ 6\ 7 \\
\hline
\end{array}
$$

2 Work out how much money each person has left.

First seen:
Book 2 Page 42

a) Abdul had £5 and spent 90p. £ [.   ]

b) Bridget had £5 and spent £3.59. £ [.   ]

c) Callum had £10 and spent £8.84. £ [.   ]

3 Fill in the missing numbers from the 11 and 12 times tables.

First seen: Book 2 Page 38

a) 2 × 11 = ☐   b) 3 × 12 = ☐   c) 5 × 12 = ☐

d) 8 × ☐ = 96   e) 9 × ☐ = 99   f) 7 × ☐ = 84

4 Round these numbers to the nearest 10.

First seen: Book 2 Page 28

a) 2267 ☐   b) 5332 ☐

c) 6235 ☐   d) 1168 ☐

e) 7822 ☐   f) 6918 ☐

g) 9242 ☐   h) 7998 ☐

5 Add these numbers together using written addition.

a) 4 5 9
  + 1 8 4

b) 3 3 3
  + 3 7 9

c) 1 3 6
  + 2 9 7

d) 7 3 7
  + 1 9 9

e) 3 4 8
  + 4 8 3

f) 3 5 5
  + 5 6 9

I spy more maths practice on the horizon...

Exercise 23

The bottom number of a fraction is called the <u>denominator</u> and the top number is called the <u>numerator</u>. In fractions with the same <u>denominator</u>, look at the <u>numerator</u> to decide which is <u>largest</u>.

1 < 3 so... $\dfrac{1}{8} < \dfrac{3}{8}$ 6 > 4 so... $\dfrac{6}{8} > \dfrac{4}{8}$

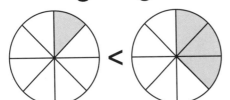   <   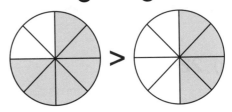   >

Put fractions with the <u>same denominator</u> in order using the <u>numerators</u>.

$$\dfrac{4}{8}, \ \dfrac{3}{8}, \ \dfrac{6}{8}, \ \dfrac{1}{8} \longrightarrow \dfrac{1}{8} < \dfrac{3}{8} < \dfrac{4}{8} < \dfrac{6}{8}$$

In order, the numerators are 1, 3, 4, 6 so...

1   Fill in the blanks with either < or >.

a) $\dfrac{1}{4} \ \boxed{<} \ \dfrac{3}{4}$ b) $\dfrac{9}{10} \ \boxed{>} \ \dfrac{8}{10}$ c) $\dfrac{2}{7} \ \boxed{<} \ \dfrac{4}{7}$

d) $\dfrac{1}{8} \ \boxed{<} \ \dfrac{7}{8}$ e) $\dfrac{5}{6} \ \boxed{>} \ \dfrac{2}{6}$ f) $\dfrac{5}{9} \ \boxed{<} \ \dfrac{8}{9}$

g) $\dfrac{4}{5} \ \boxed{>} \ \dfrac{2}{5}$ h) $\dfrac{1}{3} \ \boxed{<} \ \dfrac{2}{3}$ i) $\dfrac{3}{13} \ \boxed{>} \ \dfrac{1}{13}$

2   Use the 11 and 12 times tables to fill in the blanks.

First seen:
Book 2 Page 38

a) $121 \div 11 = \boxed{11}$ b) $96 \div 8 = \boxed{12}$ c) $99 \div 9 = \boxed{11}$

d) $88 \div 11 = \boxed{8}$ e) $\boxed{48} \div 4 = 12$ f) $84 \div \boxed{12} = 7$

3 Add these numbers together using mental arithmetic.

First seen:
Book 2 Page 40

a) 400 + 570 = **970**   b) 640 + 150 = **790**

c) 750 + 230 = **980**   d) 180 + 450 = **630**

e) 480 + 280 = **760**   f) 490 + 320 = **810**

4 Add these numbers together using written addition.

First seen:
Book 2 Page 30

a)
```
  5 ⁶6 4
+   5 7
  6 2 1
```

b)
```
 ⁴4 ²2 8
+    9 8
  5 2 6
```

c)
```
  2 4 8
+   7 4
  3 2 2
```

d)
```
 ¹1 ⁸8 6
+    7 5
  2 6 1
```

e)
```
 ²2 ⁵5 8
+    5 7
  3 1 5
```

f)
```
 ³3 ⁶6 7
+    9 4
  4 6 1
```

5 Put these fractions in order from smallest to largest.

a) $\frac{1}{5}, \frac{4}{5}, \frac{2}{5}$: $\frac{1}{5} , \frac{2}{5} , \frac{4}{5}$

b) $\frac{5}{8}, \frac{3}{8}, \frac{1}{8}$: $\frac{1}{8} , \frac{3}{8} , \frac{5}{8}$

c) $\frac{3}{7}, \frac{2}{7}, \frac{5}{7}$: $\frac{2}{7} , \frac{3}{7} , \frac{5}{7}$

d) $\frac{2}{4}, \frac{3}{4}, \frac{1}{4}$: $\frac{1}{4} , \frac{2}{4} , \frac{3}{4}$

e) $\frac{1}{9}, \frac{8}{9}, \frac{5}{9}$: $\frac{1}{9} , \frac{5}{9} , \frac{8}{9}$

f) $\frac{10}{12}, \frac{4}{12}, \frac{7}{12}$: $\frac{4}{12} , \frac{7}{12} , \frac{10}{12}$

Don't overload your circuits — take a break if you need one...

Exercise 24

Mental multiplication of bigger numbers

When multiplying <u>tens</u> by a number, multiply the digit
in the <u>tens column</u> by the number...

$$\underline{3}0 \times 6 = ? \quad \longrightarrow \quad \underline{3} \times 6 = 18$$

↖ 30 has <u>3 tens</u>...   ↖ ...so do **3 × 6.**

Hundreds	Tens	Ones
	1	8
1	8	0

...then move all the digits <u>one place</u>
to the <u>left</u> and fill the gap with a <u>0</u>.

So 30 × 6 = 180

① **Multiply these numbers together using mental arithmetic.**

a) 40 × 7 = 280   b) 60 × 8 = 480   c) 20 × 4 = 80

d) 30 × 5 = 150   e) 80 × 7 = 560   f) 60 × 6 = 366

g) 20 × 11 = 220   h) 90 × 10 = 900   i) 70 × 9 = 630

② **Tick the boxes next to the true statements.**

First seen:
Book 2 Page 46

a) $\frac{4}{8} > \frac{1}{8}$ ✓   b) $\frac{3}{9} < \frac{6}{9}$ ✓   c) $\frac{2}{4} > \frac{3}{4}$ ✗

d) $\frac{1}{10} > \frac{5}{10}$ ✓   e) $\frac{3}{6} < \frac{2}{6}$ ✗   f) $\frac{5}{7} < \frac{6}{7}$ ✓

g) $\frac{7}{17} < \frac{12}{17}$ ✓   h) $\frac{16}{20} > \frac{14}{20}$ ✓   i) $\frac{3}{11} > \frac{9}{11}$ ✗

j) $\frac{4}{14} > \frac{1}{14}$ ✓   k) $\frac{12}{13} < \frac{7}{13}$ ✗   l) $\frac{3}{12} > \frac{4}{12}$ ✗

3 Fill in the blanks to do these subtractions with money.

First seen: Book 2 Page 42

a) £4.50 – 70p = £ 3.20

b) £2.51 – £1.52 = £ 0.99

c) £5.54 – 98p = £ 4.56

d) £7.48 – £5.68 = £ 1.80

e) £1.23 – 57p = £ 0.66

f) £4.65 – £2.88 = £ 1.77

4 Fill in the missing numbers.

First seen: Book 2 Page 32

a) 600 – 475 = 125

b) 800 – 627 = 173

c) 200 – 164 = 36

d) 500 – 331 = 169

e) 400 – 187 = 213

f) 800 – 558 = 242

g) 300 – 113 = 187

h) 700 – 362 = 338

5 Use mental arithmetic to multiply these numbers.

a) 30 × 2 = 60

b) 50 × 6 = 300

c) 90 × 4 = 360

d) 40 × 9 = 360

e) 20 × 12 = 240

f) 70 × 7 = 490

g) 80 × 3 = 240

h) 60 × 11 = 660

i) 40 × 5 = 200

There are more questions on the next page? Race you there...

Exercise 25

Written subtraction with two-digit numbers

Write the first number on top of the second, lining up the columns.
Subtract the bottom digit from the top in the ones column, then the tens.

$89 - 25 = ?$

Tens Ones

```
   8 9
 - 2 5
     4
```
$9 - 5 = \underline{4}$

Tens Ones

```
   8 9
 - 2 5
   6 4
```
$8 - 2 = \underline{6}$

So $89 - 25 = 64$

---

1 Use written subtraction to subtract these numbers.

a)
```
   8 9
 - 5 4
   3 5
```

b)
```
   9 6
 - 3 2
   3 4
```

c)
```
   5 2
 - 4 1
   1 1
```

d)
```
   6 6
 - 2 3
   4 3
```

e)
```
   9 8
 - 7 7
   2 1
```

f)
```
   3 5
 - 1 1
   2 4
```

g)
```
   2 6
 - 1 5
   1 1
```

h)
```
   4 7
 - 3 6
   1 1
```

2 Use mental arithmetic to multiply these numbers.

First seen:
Book 2 Page 48

a) $10 \times 3 =$ 30

b) $20 \times 5 =$ 100

c) $60 \times 4 =$ 240

d) $90 \times 8 =$ 720

e) $70 \times 10 =$ 700

f) $40 \times 3 =$ 120

g) $80 \times 2 =$ 160

h) $30 \times 8 =$ 240

i) $50 \times 8 =$ 400

3 Use written addition to add these numbers.

First seen: Book 2 Page 44

a)
```
  ¹1 ⁵5 6
+  6 7 8
―――――――
   8 3 4
```

b)
```
  ⁴4 ⁶6 7
+  3 5 6
―――――――
   8 2 3
```

c)
```
  ⁵5 7 4
+  3 5 9
―――――――
   9 3 3
```

d)
```
  ¹2 ⁵5 8
+  4 6 2
―――――――
   7 2 0
```

e)
```
  ⁷7 8 4
+  1 5 7
―――――――
   9 4 1
```

f)
```
  ⁵5 ⁵5 4
+  3 6 7
―――――――
   9 2 1
```

4 Add these amounts of money.

First seen: Book 2 Page 34

a) £2.49 + £4.41 = £ 6 . 90

b) £3.70 + £2.80 = £ 6 . 50

c) £3.67 + £4.82 = £ 8 . 49

d) £7.28 + £2.01 = £ 9 . 29

e) £4.86 + £1.20 = £ 6 . 06

f) £5.45 + £3.55 = £ 9 . 00

g) £5.87 + £1.31 = £ 7 . 18

h) £6.39 + £0.85 = £ 7 . 24

5 Subtract these numbers using written subtraction.

a)
```
  5 5
- 4 2
―――――
  1 3
```

b)
```
  2 8
- 1 3
―――――
  1 5
```

c)
```
  3 9
- 2 4
―――――
  1 5
```

d)
```
  9 2
- 6 1
―――――
  3 1
```

e)
```
  7 9
- 5 3
―――――
  2 6
```

f)
```
  2 2
- 1 0
―――――
  1 2
```

g)
```
  6 5
- 4 1
―――――
  2 4
```

h)
```
  5 7
- 2 0
―――――
  3 7
```

Don't skip a beat — move on to the next page...

Exercise 26

Rounding four-digit numbers

To round to the nearest <u>hundred</u>, check the column to the <u>right</u>, the <u>tens</u>.
To round to the nearest <u>thousand</u>, check the column to the <u>right</u>, the <u>hundreds</u>.
If the digit in this column is <u>less than 5</u>, round <u>down</u>.
If it's <u>5 or more</u>, round <u>up</u>.

To the nearest <u>hundred</u>:

Tens

1 2 <u>4</u> 7 ➡ 1 <u>2 0 0</u>

There are <u>4 tens</u>,
so round <u>down</u> to <u>1200</u>.

To the nearest <u>thousand</u>:

Hundreds

4 <u>7</u> 8 9 ➡ <u>5 0 0 0</u>

There are <u>7 hundreds</u>,
so round <u>up</u> to <u>5000</u>.

1 Circle the option that makes each sentence correct.

a) 5236 rounded to the nearest 100 is: (5200) or 5300

b) 1562 rounded to the nearest 100 is: 1500 or (1600)

c) 2486 rounded to the nearest 100 is: 2400 or (2500)

d) 6186 rounded to the nearest 1000 is: (6000) or (7000)

e) 8525 rounded to the nearest 1000 is: 8000 or 9000

f) 3620 rounded to the nearest 1000 is: 3000 or 4000

2 Use written subtraction to subtract these numbers.

First seen:
Book 2 Page 50

a) 3 8
− 2 3

b) 4 9
− 1 1

c) 5 8
− 3 8

d) 6 6
− 4 3

e) 9 7
− 8 6

f) 7 5
− 5 2

g) 8 4
− 7 1

h) 2 9
− 1 0

3 Fill in the blanks with either < or >.

First seen: Book 2 Page 46

a) $\dfrac{2}{5}$ ☐ $\dfrac{4}{5}$ 　b) $\dfrac{7}{11}$ ☐ $\dfrac{3}{11}$ 　c) $\dfrac{7}{8}$ ☐ $\dfrac{8}{8}$

d) $\dfrac{1}{4}$ ☐ $\dfrac{3}{4}$ 　e) $\dfrac{4}{6}$ ☐ $\dfrac{3}{6}$ 　f) $\dfrac{2}{7}$ ☐ $\dfrac{4}{7}$

g) $\dfrac{2}{3}$ ☐ $\dfrac{1}{3}$ 　h) $\dfrac{14}{15}$ ☐ $\dfrac{4}{15}$ 　i) $\dfrac{6}{10}$ ☐ $\dfrac{5}{10}$

4 Add these numbers together using written addition.

First seen: Book 2 Page 36

a) 　2 6 5 + 3 5 2

b) 　4 9 0 + 4 2 4

c) 　7 4 8 + 2 1 3

d) 　5 5 7 + 1 2 5

e) 　3 2 8 + 5 9 1

f) 　5 6 8 + 2 5 1

5 Round the numbers to complete the table.

	Number	To the nearest 100	To the nearest 1000
a)	8541		
b)	2936		
c)	3492		
d)	1364		

What's that you say? Oh, there's more maths practice over the page...

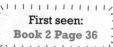

Exercise 27

Mental arithmetic using times tables

Once you know all the times tables by heart,
you can use them to multiply and divide pairs of numbers.
Numbers can be swapped around in a multiplication and you'll
still get the same answer, but this is not true for division.

$$3 \times 4 = 12$$
$$4 \times 3 = 12$$

4 groups of 3 →

← 3 groups of 4

$$12 \div 4 = 3$$
$$12 \div 3 = 4$$

But, $4 \div 12$ is not 3
$3 \div 12$ is not 4

---

(1) Fill in the missing symbols (× or ÷) using the times tables.

a) $4 \times 5 = 5 \;\boxed{}\; 4$　　b) $36 \;\boxed{}\; 12 = 3$　　c) $7 \;\boxed{}\; 8 = 56$

d) $144 \;\boxed{}\; 12 = 12$　　e) $4 \;\boxed{}\; 8 = 8 \times 4$　　f) $2 \times 9 = 9 \;\boxed{}\; 2$

g) $12 \;\boxed{}\; 9 = 9 \times 12$　　h) $24 \;\boxed{}\; 6 = 4$　　i) $55 \;\boxed{}\; 11 = 5$

---

(2) Round each number to the nearest hundred, then thousand, as shown.

First seen: Book 2 Page 52

a) 8754: **8800** **9000**　　b) 3879: _____ _____

c) 5421: _____ _____　　d) 1748: _____ _____

e) 6587: _____ _____　　f) 4256: _____ _____

g) 7615: _____ _____　　h) 2798: _____ _____

---

3 Put these fractions in order from largest to smallest.

First seen: Book 2 Page 46

a) $\dfrac{5}{10}, \dfrac{7}{10}, \dfrac{3}{10}:$ ____ , ____ , ____

b) $\dfrac{2}{4}, \dfrac{1}{4}, \dfrac{3}{4}:$ ____ , ____ , ____

c) $\dfrac{4}{5}, \dfrac{2}{5}, \dfrac{3}{5}:$ ____ , ____ , ____

d) $\dfrac{8}{9}, \dfrac{5}{9}, \dfrac{3}{9}:$ ____ , ____ , ____

4 Add these numbers using mental arithmetic.

First seen: Book 2 Page 40

a) 150 + 740 = ____

b) 360 + 240 = ____

c) 740 + 170 = ____

d) 470 + 350 = ____

e) 580 + 250 = ____

f) 670 + 180 = ____

g) 390 + 240 = ____

h) 470 + 190 = ____

5 Use the times tables to fill in the blanks.

a) 3 × ____ = 33

b) ____ × 8 = 72

c) ____ ÷ 6 = 5

d) 110 = ____ × 11

e) 18 ÷ ____ = 6

f) 9 × ____ = 63

g) ____ ÷ 8 = 12

h) ____ × 4 = 48

i) ____ × 5 = 35

Keep on going, you'll crack it eventually...

Finding unit fractions of a number

Unit fractions have 1 as the numerator ('top number'). To find a unit fraction of a number, divide the number by the denominator ('bottom number').

$\frac{1}{3}$ of 12
$= 12 \div 3 = 4$

$\frac{1}{4}$ of 36
$= 36 \div 4 = 9$

1 Find the following fractions of numbers.

a) $\frac{1}{4}$ of 16 = ☐ b) $\frac{1}{3}$ of 9 = ☐ c) $\frac{1}{7}$ of 21 = ☐

d) $\frac{1}{10}$ of 100 = ☐ e) $\frac{1}{2}$ of 24 = ☐ f) $\frac{1}{5}$ of 25 = ☐

g) $\frac{1}{8}$ of 32 = ☐ h) $\frac{1}{6}$ of 30 = ☐ i) $\frac{1}{3}$ of 15 = ☐

2 Fill in the blanks with amounts of money.

First seen: Book 2 Page 42

a) £5.65 – 25p = £ ☐ . 　 b) £4.80 – £1.90 = £ ☐ .

c) £9.52 – 60p = £ ☐ . 　 d) £8.39 – £3.45 = £ ☐ .

e) £2.46 – 56p = £ ☐ . 　 f) £6.35 – £2.47 = £ ☐ .

g) £3.54 – 45p = £ ☐ . 　 h) £5.28 – £1.34 = £ ☐ .

3 Fill in the blanks using written subtraction.

First seen: Book 2 Page 50

a)
```
  2 3
- 1 1
-----
```

b)
```
  7 8
- 2 4
-----
```

c)
```
  4 5
- 3 2
-----
```

d)
```
  9 9
- 7 6
-----
```

e)
```
  8 6
- 4 3
-----
```

f)
```
  3 8
- 1 5
-----
```

g)
```
  5 7
- 3 3
-----
```

h)
```
  6 8
- 4 1
-----
```

4 Use the 11 and 12 times tables to fill in the missing numbers.

First seen: Book 2 Page 38

a) $55 \div 5 =$ ☐   b) $24 \div 2 =$ ☐   c) $44 \div 11 =$ ☐

d) $24 \div 12 =$ ☐   e) $84 \div 7 =$ ☐   f) $110 \div 10 =$ ☐

g) $121 \div$ ☐ $= 11$ h) $36 \div$ ☐ $= 12$ i) ☐ $\div 11 = 6$

5 Fill in the missing numbers.

a) $\frac{1}{6}$ of 42 = ☐   b) $\frac{1}{8}$ of 56 = ☐   c) $\frac{1}{11}$ of 44 = ☐

d) $\frac{1}{12}$ of 60 = ☐   e) $\frac{1}{7}$ of 63 = ☐   f) $\frac{1}{9}$ of 27 = ☐

g) $\frac{1}{4}$ of 16 = ☐   h) $\frac{1}{3}$ of 27 = ☐   i) $\frac{1}{2}$ of 14 = ☐

Now the real question is, what fraction of this cake can I eat...

Exercise 29

Write the first number on top of the second, lining up the columns.
Subtract the bottom digit from the top in each column. If the top digit
is smaller than the bottom, exchange from the column to the left.

$$67 - 38 = ?$$

Subtract the ones...

Tens Ones
5   17
$\cancel{6}\,\cancel{7}$
$-\ 3\ 8$
_____
$\quad\ 9$

7 is smaller than
8, so exchange
1 ten for 10 ones.
10 + 7 = 17
17 − 8 = 9

...then subtract the tens.

Tens Ones
5   17
$\cancel{6}\,\cancel{7}$
$-\ 3\ 8$
_____
$\ 2\ 9$

There's now 1 less ten
here because you
changed a ten into ones.
5 − 3 = 2

So 67 − 38 = 29

1 Use written subtraction to subtract these numbers.

a)   7 2
  − 3 4

b)   6 8
  − 1 9

c)   4 6
  − 2 7

d)   7 5
  − 4 6

e)   9 8
  − 2 9

f)   5 4
  − 2 6

g)   3 7
  − 1 8

h)   4 5
  − 3 9

First seen: Book 2 Page 56

2 Find the following fractions of numbers.

a) $\frac{1}{3}$ of 30 =

b) $\frac{1}{8}$ of 64 =

c) $\frac{1}{9}$ of 108 =

d) $\frac{1}{11}$ of 99 =

e) $\frac{1}{12}$ of 36 =

f) $\frac{1}{7}$ of 35 =

3 Tick the boxes next to the numbers that have been rounded correctly to the nearest 100.

First seen:
Book 2 Page 52

a) 2569 ⟶ 2600 ☐

b) 9634 ⟶ 9700 ☐

c) 8425 ⟶ 8000 ☐

d) 1478 ⟶ 1500 ☐

e) 7951 ⟶ 8000 ☐

f) 4112 ⟶ 4100 ☐

4 Use the times tables to fill in the blanks.

First seen:
Book 2 Page 54

a) 4 × 5 = ☐

b) 12 × 3 = ☐

c) 70 ÷ 7 = ☐

d) 11 × 4 = ☐

e) 54 ÷ 9 = ☐

f) 9 × 7 = ☐

g) 10 ÷ 2 = ☐

h) 8 × 9 = ☐

i) 12 × 5 = ☐

5 Subtract these numbers using written subtraction.

a)
```
   2 6
 - 1 8
 ─────
```

b)
```
   5 4
 - 3 5
 ─────
```

c)
```
   8 8
 - 7 9
 ─────
```

d)
```
   4 3
 - 2 7
 ─────
```

e)
```
   7 6
 - 3 7
 ─────
```

f)
```
   3 7
 - 1 9
 ─────
```

g)
```
   6 2
 - 3 5
 ─────
```

h)
```
   9 5
 - 4 9
 ─────
```

Don't overload yourself — give yourself a break...

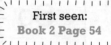

Exercise 30

Finding non-unit fractions of a number

To find any fraction of a number, first <u>divide</u> the number by the <u>denominator</u> (bottom number) then <u>multiply</u> by the <u>numerator</u> (top number).

$$\frac{5}{8} \text{ of } 24 = ?$$

$$\frac{1}{8} \text{ of } 24 = 24 \div 8 = 3$$

So $\frac{5}{8}$ of 24 = 3 × 5 = 15

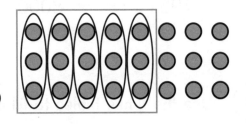

1 Find the following fractions of numbers.

a) $\frac{1}{4}$ of 12 =

$\frac{3}{4}$ of 12 =

b) $\frac{1}{5}$ of 40 =

$\frac{2}{5}$ of 40 =

c) $\frac{1}{7}$ of 28 =

$\frac{4}{7}$ of 28 =

d) $\frac{1}{8}$ of 64 =

$\frac{5}{8}$ of 64 =

e) $\frac{1}{6}$ of 30 =

$\frac{5}{6}$ of 30 =

f) $\frac{1}{9}$ of 81 =

$\frac{8}{9}$ of 81 =

2 Use written subtraction to subtract these numbers.

First seen:
Book 2 Page 58

a)
```
  8 2
- 6 4
```

b)
```
  9 2
- 7 6
```

c)
```
  5 8
- 2 9
```

d)
```
  7 6
- 5 8
```

e)
```
  2 3
- 1 5
```

f)
```
  3 5
- 1 6
```

g)
```
  6 3
- 4 7
```

h)
```
  6 6
- 3 7
```

3   **Use the times tables to fill in the blanks.**

First seen: Book 2 Page 54

a) 6 × 12 = ⬚   b) 7 × 3 = ⬚   c) 90 ÷ 9 = ⬚

d) 4 × 5 = ⬚   e) 45 ÷ 9 = ⬚   f) 8 × 11 = ⬚

g) 44 ÷ 4 = ⬚   h) 12 × 11 = ⬚   i) 2 × 6 = ⬚

4   **Use written addition to add these numbers together.**

First seen: Book 2 Page 44

a)
```
   2  3  5
+  5  7  6
```

b)
```
   4  8  9
+  2  5  1
```

c)
```
   2  4  4
+  1  7  8
```

d)
```
   6  2  6
+  2  9  5
```

e)
```
   5  6  8
+  3  7  9
```

f)
```
   2  9  9
+  2  5  3
```

5   **Fill in the missing numbers.**

a) $\frac{7}{8}$ of 80 = ⬚   b) $\frac{5}{12}$ of 36 = ⬚   c) $\frac{4}{11}$ of 55 = ⬚

d) $\frac{3}{10}$ of 100 = ⬚   e) $\frac{4}{5}$ of 20 = ⬚   f) $\frac{3}{7}$ of 42 = ⬚

Which way to the next Exercise? Try over the page...

Exercise 31

Written subtraction with three-digit numbers

Subtract the <u>bottom digit</u> from the <u>top</u> in each column. If the top digit is <u>smaller</u> than the bottom, <u>exchange</u> from the <u>column to the left</u>.

$$862 - 123 = ?$$

First subtract the <u>ones</u>...   ...then the <u>tens</u>...   ...then the <u>hundreds</u>.

```
  H  T  O              H  T  O              H  T  O
     5 12                 5 12                 5 12
  8  6̸ 2̸              8  6̸ 2̸              8  6̸ 2̸
- 1  2  3            - 1  2  3            - 1  2  3
--------            --------            --------
        9                 3  9              7  3  9
```

2 is smaller than 3, so <u>exchange 1 ten</u> for <u>10 ones</u>.
10 + 2 = 12
12 – 3 = <u>9</u>.

The 6 tens is now 5 tens.
5 tens – 2 tens = <u>3 tens</u>.

8 hundreds – 1 hundred = <u>7 hundreds</u>.

$$862 - 123 = 739$$

1 Use written subtraction to fill in the blanks.

a)
```
   2  5  3
 - 1  1  8
```

b)
```
   4  7  5
 - 3  2  7
```

c)
```
   5  3  2
 - 2  0  6
```

d)
```
   6  1  4
 - 2  5  3
```

e)
```
   7  2  6
 - 4  9  1
```

f)
```
   8  4  9
 - 6  8  2
```

2 Fill in the missing numbers.

First seen: Book 2 Page 48

a) 20 × 3 = ☐   b) 40 × 5 = ☐   c) 90 × 6 = ☐

d) 70 × ☐ = 280   e) 80 × ☐ = 160   f) ☐ × 7 = 210

3 Use written subtraction to fill in the missing numbers.

First seen: Book 2 Page 58

a)
```
  6 2
- 3 5
```

b)
```
  5 3
- 1 9
```

c)
```
  4 7
- 2 8
```

d)
```
  7 1
- 4 3
```

e)
```
  8 6
- 5 7
```

f)
```
  3 4
- 2 6
```

g)
```
  9 5
- 7 6
```

h)
```
  6 4
- 5 7
```

4 Fill in the blanks to find these fractions of numbers.

First seen: Book 2 Page 60

a) $\frac{1}{5}$ of 20 =

$\frac{2}{5}$ of 20 =

b) $\frac{1}{8}$ of 32 =

$\frac{3}{8}$ of 32 =

c) $\frac{1}{5}$ of 40 =

$\frac{4}{5}$ of 40 =

d) $\frac{1}{6}$ of 42 =

$\frac{5}{6}$ of 42 =

e) $\frac{1}{8}$ of 24 =

$\frac{7}{8}$ of 24 =

f) $\frac{1}{7}$ of 28 =

$\frac{5}{7}$ of 28 =

5 Work out the answers using written subtraction.

a)
```
  6 8 6
- 1 4 7
```

b)
```
  5 7 4
- 3 8 4
```

c)
```
  2 6 1
- 2 3 9
```

d)
```
  3 7 5
- 2 8 4
```

e)
```
  5 4 6
- 4 1 8
```

f)
```
  9 0 8
- 5 1 7
```

Exchange ten minutes for one break...

Exercise 32

Mental division using the times tables

Use <u>times table facts</u> to divide <u>multiples of ten</u> by numbers up to 12.
The answer will be a <u>multiple of ten</u>.

$$18 \div 6 = 3 \qquad\qquad 35 \div 5 = 7$$
$$\text{So } 18\underline{0} \div 6 = 3\underline{0} \qquad \text{So } 35\underline{0} \div 5 = 7\underline{0}$$

(1) **Fill in the blanks to divide these multiples of ten.**

a) $6 \div 3 = 2$

$60 \div 3 = $ ☐

b) $16 \div 4 = 4$

$160 \div 4 = $ ☐

c) $45 \div 5 = 9$

$450 \div 5 = $ ☐

d) $30 \div 6 = 5$

$300 \div 6 = $ ☐

e) $27 \div 9 = 3$

$270 \div 9 = $ ☐

f) $48 \div 8 = 6$

$480 \div 8 = $ ☐

g) $56 \div 7 = 8$

$560 \div 7 = $ ☐

h) $88 \div 8 = 11$

$880 \div 8 = $ ☐

i) $72 \div 12 = 6$

$720 \div 12 = $ ☐

(2) **Use written subtraction to fill in the blanks.**

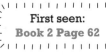
First seen:
Book 2 Page 62

a)
```
   3  2  1
-  2  3  1
_____
```
☐

b)
```
   8  3  4
-  4  1  5
_____
```
☐

c)
```
   7  6  9
-  6  8  4
_____
```
☐

d)
```
   5  5  2
-  3  3  8
_____
```
☐

e)
```
   4  0  6
-  2  6  0
_____
```
☐

f)
```
   6  4  3
-  5  1  8
_____
```
☐

3 Fill in the missing numbers.

First seen:
Book 2 Page 48

a) $90 \times \boxed{} = 180$ b) $70 \times 6 = \boxed{}$ c) $\boxed{} \times 4 = 320$

d) $40 \times 12 = \boxed{}$ e) $60 \times \boxed{} = 720$ f) $\boxed{} \times 9 = 630$

g) $\boxed{} \times 11 = 880$ h) $110 \times 12 = \boxed{}$ i) $50 \times \boxed{} = 400$

4 Tick the boxes next to the true statements.

First seen:
Book 2 Page 56

a) $\frac{1}{3}$ of 12 = 4 $\square$ b) $\frac{1}{4}$ of 20 = 10 $\square$ c) $\frac{1}{5}$ of 8 = 40 $\square$

d) $\frac{1}{8}$ of 40 = 5 $\square$ e) $\frac{1}{3}$ of 36 = 9 $\square$ f) $\frac{1}{7}$ of 56 = 8 $\square$

g) $\frac{1}{5}$ of 60 = 6 $\square$ h) $\frac{1}{10}$ of 10 = 1 $\square$ i) $\frac{1}{6}$ of 42 = 8 $\square$

5 Divide these numbers using times tables facts.

a) $80 \div 2 = \boxed{}$ b) $120 \div 3 = \boxed{}$ c) $150 \div 5 = \boxed{}$

d) $440 \div 11 = \boxed{}$ e) $360 \div 3 = \boxed{}$ f) $810 \div 9 = \boxed{}$

Your next helping of delicious maths is just over the page...

Exercise 33

Comparing and ordering fractions

Unit fractions have 1 as the numerator ('top number'). The bigger the denominator ('bottom number') of a unit fraction, the smaller the fraction.

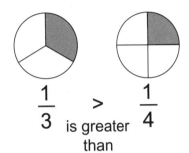

$$\frac{1}{3} > \frac{1}{4}$$
is greater than

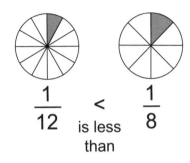

$$\frac{1}{12} < \frac{1}{8}$$
is less than

Write unit fractions in size order by their denominators:

$$\frac{1}{12} < \frac{1}{8} < \frac{1}{4} < \frac{1}{3}$$

Fractions increasing (smallest to largest)

Denominators decreasing

---

(1) Fill in the blanks with either < or >.

a) $\frac{1}{2} \; \square \; \frac{1}{3}$

c) $\frac{1}{3} \; \square \; \frac{1}{5}$

b) $\frac{1}{4} \; \square \; \frac{1}{2}$

d) $\frac{1}{6} \; \square \; \frac{1}{4}$

e) $\frac{1}{5} \; \square \; \frac{1}{7}$

f) $\frac{1}{10} \; \square \; \frac{1}{8}$

g) $\frac{1}{8} \; \square \; \frac{1}{16}$

i) $\frac{1}{12} \; \square \; \frac{1}{13}$

h) $\frac{1}{20} \; \square \; \frac{1}{10}$

---

(2) Fill in the missing numbers.

First seen:
Book 2 Page 50

a)
```
   7  8
-  2  7
_____
```

b)
```
   4  4
-  2  1
_____
```

c)
```
   6  9
-  5  6
_____
```

d)
```
   9  8
-  7  3
_____
```

3 Circle the correct option to complete each sentence.

First seen:
Book 2 Page 60

a) $\frac{3}{5}$ of 15 is: 9 or 10

b) $\frac{5}{6}$ of 12 is: 10 or 11

c) $\frac{5}{8}$ of 32 is: 20 or 25

d) $\frac{2}{7}$ of 56 is: 16 or 18

e) $\frac{3}{8}$ of 160 is: 40 or 60

f) $\frac{4}{5}$ of 100 is: 40 or 80

4 Use times tables facts to divide these numbers.

First seen:
Book 2 Page 64

a) 160 ÷ 8 =

b) 480 ÷ 4 =

c) 540 ÷ 6 =

d) 240 ÷ 3 =

e) 630 ÷ 9 =

f) 250 ÷ 5 =

5 Write the fractions in size order from smallest to largest.

a) $\frac{1}{7}, \frac{1}{4}, \frac{1}{5}$: , ,

b) $\frac{1}{3}, \frac{1}{6}, \frac{1}{9}$: , ,

c) $\frac{1}{8}, \frac{1}{4}, \frac{1}{6}$: , ,

d) $\frac{1}{10}, \frac{1}{2}, \frac{1}{5}$: , ,

e) $\frac{1}{15}, \frac{1}{12}, \frac{1}{25}$: , ,

f) $\frac{1}{8}, \frac{1}{10}, \frac{1}{9}$: , ,

Unit fractions? I knit scarves...

Exercise 34

Mental addition of multiples of 100

<u>Partition</u> one number into <u>thousands</u> and <u>hundreds</u> and add them <u>separately</u>.

$$2300 + 6800 = ?$$

$6800 = \underline{6\ thousands} + \underline{8\ hundreds}$

Add 6000...

$$2\underline{3}00 + \underline{6}000 = \underline{83}00$$

...then add 800.

$$\underline{83}00 + \underline{8}00 = \underline{91}00$$

Or you could <u>add</u> the number of <u>hundreds</u>:

$$2\underline{3}00 + \underline{68}00 = \underline{91}00$$

$\underline{23}$ hundreds + $\underline{68}$ hundreds = $\underline{91}$ hundreds

---

1 Add these numbers using mental arithmetic.

a) 1500 + 2400 = [ ]

b) 3200 + 1300 = [ ]

c) 4600 + 3100 = [ ]

d) 2800 + 3400 = [ ]

e) 5300 + 3800 = [ ]

f) 1700 + 7400 = [ ]

---

2 Circle the largest fraction in each set of three.

First seen:
Book 2 Page 66

a) $\dfrac{1}{10}$, $\dfrac{1}{3}$, $\dfrac{1}{5}$

b) $\dfrac{1}{6}$, $\dfrac{1}{60}$, $\dfrac{1}{16}$

c) $\dfrac{1}{2}$, $\dfrac{1}{3}$, $\dfrac{1}{4}$

d) $\dfrac{1}{8}$, $\dfrac{1}{12}$, $\dfrac{1}{4}$

e) $\dfrac{1}{100}$, $\dfrac{1}{200}$, $\dfrac{1}{50}$

f) $\dfrac{1}{11}$, $\dfrac{1}{101}$, $\dfrac{1}{111}$

---

3 Fill in the missing numbers.

First seen: Book 2 Page 52

a) 1234 rounded to the nearest 100 is [ ] .

b) 6543 rounded to the nearest 1000 is [ ] .

c) 8765 rounded to the nearest [ ] is 9000.

d) 9462 rounded to the nearest [ ] is 9500.

e) 2950 is [ ] when rounded to the nearest 100 or 1000.

4 Use written subtraction to fill in the blanks.

First seen: Book 2 Page 62

a)
```
    6  8  1
 -  5  3  4
```
[ ]

b)
```
    7  0  9
 -  2  3  6
```
[ ]

c)
```
    8  2  8
 -  4  4  4
```
[ ]

d)
```
    5  3  0
 -  2  0  7
```
[ ]

e)
```
    9  8  9
 -  1  9  8
```
[ ]

f)
```
    4  7  3
 -  3  5  6
```
[ ]

5 Fill in the missing numbers.

a) 3400 + 4600 = [ ]

b) 4200 + 1600 = [ ]

c) 3900 + 4200 = [ ]

d) 7100 + 1800 = [ ]

e) 1200 + 1700 = [ ]

f) 1600 + 2700 = [ ]

After all those big numbers, turn the page for something smaller...

Exercise 35

Arithmetic with fractions

To <u>add</u> or <u>subtract</u> fractions with the <u>same denominator</u> ('bottom number'), add or subtract the <u>numerators</u> ('top numbers') <u>only</u>.

$$1 + 2 = \underline{3}$$
$$\frac{1}{5} + \frac{2}{5} = \frac{3}{5}$$

$$11 - 6 = \underline{5}$$
$$\frac{11}{12} - \frac{6}{12} = \frac{5}{12}$$

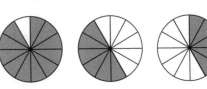

(1) Fill in the blanks to add these pairs of fractions.

a) $\frac{1}{4} + \frac{2}{4} = \frac{\boxed{}}{4}$

b) $\frac{5}{7} + \frac{1}{7} = \frac{\boxed{}}{7}$

c) $\frac{2}{9} + \frac{5}{9} = \frac{\boxed{}}{9}$

d) $\frac{3}{5} + \frac{1}{5} = \boxed{}$

e) $\frac{2}{6} + \frac{3}{6} = \boxed{}$

f) $\frac{7}{10} + \frac{2}{10} = \boxed{}$

g) $\frac{7}{15} + \frac{4}{15} = \boxed{}$

h) $\frac{9}{17} + \frac{3}{17} = \boxed{}$

i) $\frac{8}{20} + \frac{9}{20} = \boxed{}$

(2) Use times tables facts to fill in the missing numbers.

First seen: Book 2 Page 64

a) $490 \div 7 = \boxed{}$

b) $360 \div \boxed{} = 40$

c) $\boxed{} \div 3 = 70$

d) $240 \div \boxed{} = 30$

e) $720 \div 9 = \boxed{}$

f) $\boxed{} \div 6 = 50$

(3) Fill in the blanks to find these fractions of numbers.

First seen: Book 2 Page 56

a) $\frac{1}{3}$ of 36 = ▢

b) $\frac{1}{5}$ of 55 = ▢

c) $\frac{1}{7}$ of 63 = ▢

d) $\frac{1}{6}$ of 72 = ▢

e) $\frac{1}{8}$ of 72 = ▢

f) $\frac{1}{9}$ of 45 = ▢

(4) Add these numbers using mental arithmetic.

First seen: Book 2 Page 68

a) 2600 + 3500 = ▢

b) 4100 + 4900 = ▢

c) 5500 + 3700 = ▢

d) 3300 + 4800 = ▢

e) 6900 + 2800 = ▢

f) 1600 + 7700 = ▢

(5) Fill in the blanks to subtract these fractions.

a) $\frac{4}{5} - \frac{2}{5} = \frac{▢}{5}$

b) $\frac{6}{8} - \frac{5}{8} = \frac{▢}{8}$

c) $\frac{9}{10} - \frac{2}{10} = \frac{▢}{10}$

d) $\frac{5}{6} - \frac{4}{6} = ▢$

e) $\frac{6}{7} - \frac{4}{7} = ▢$

f) $\frac{11}{13} - \frac{2}{13} = ▢$

g) $\frac{15}{19} - \frac{7}{19} = ▢$

h) $\frac{17}{20} - \frac{14}{20} = ▢$

i) $\frac{24}{25} - \frac{5}{25} = ▢$

Lights, camera, fraction...

Exercise 36

Written subtraction with three-digit numbers

For some written subtractions, you might have to exchange more than once.

$$715 - 428 = ?$$

First subtract the ones...   ...then the tens...   ...then the hundreds.

```
  H  T  O
     0 15
  7  X̶ 5̶
- 4  2  8
_____
        7
```

5 is smaller than 8,
so exchange 1 ten for
10 ones to give
15 − 8 = 7.

```
  H   T   O
  6 10 0̶  15
  7̶  X̶  5̶
- 4   2   8
_____
      8   7
```

The 1 ten is now 0 tens.
This is smaller than 2 tens,
so exchange 1 hundred
for 10 tens to give
10 tens − 2 tens = 8 tens.

```
  H   T   O
  6 10 0̶  15
  7̶  X̶  5̶
- 4   2   8
_____
  2   8   7
```

The 7 hundreds is
now 6 hundreds.
6 hundreds
− 4 hundreds
= 2 hundreds.

1 Use written subtraction to fill in the blanks.

a)
```
  3  3  5
- 1  5  8
```

b)
```
  4  2  6
- 2  2  7
```

c)
```
  6  4  1
- 3  7  5
```

d)
```
  5  5  3
- 2  9  6
```

e)
```
  7  1  2
- 4  8  3
```

f)
```
  8  6  4
- 5  6  9
```

2 Fill in the missing fractions.

First seen: Book 2 Page 70

a) $\frac{3}{10} + \frac{4}{10} = \boxed{}$

b) $\frac{3}{9} + \frac{1}{9} = \boxed{}$

c) $\frac{5}{11} + \frac{5}{11} = \boxed{}$

d) $\frac{5}{7} - \boxed{} = \frac{2}{7}$

e) $\frac{13}{17} - \frac{6}{17} = \boxed{}$

f) $\boxed{} - \frac{6}{15} = \frac{8}{15}$

3 Fill in the missing numbers.

First seen: Book 2 Page 68

a) 6600 + 2600 = [ ]

b) 4200 + [ ] = 6100

c) [ ] + 1800 = 4300

d) 3700 + 2300 = [ ]

e) 7300 + [ ] = 9100

f) [ ] + 2700 = 5400

4 Tick the boxes next to the true statements.

First seen: Book 2 Page 54

a) 8 × 9 = 9 × 8 [ ]

b) 42 ÷ 6 = 7 [ ]

c) 56 ÷ 8 = 6 [ ]

d) 6 ÷ 2 = 2 ÷ 6 [ ]

e) 84 ÷ 12 = 7 [ ]

f) 11 × 10 = 111 [ ]

g) 96 ÷ 8 = 12 [ ]

h) 4 × 3 > 3 × 4 [ ]

i) 12 × 12 = 132 [ ]

5 Fill in the blanks using written subtraction.

a)
```
   3 4 5
 - 2 7 6
 -------
```

b)
```
   5 6 4
 - 3 6 8
 -------
```

c)
```
   4 4 7
 - 1 9 8
 -------
```

d)
```
   7 2 5
 - 3 6 6
 -------
```

e)
```
   8 3 4
 - 6 8 7
 -------
```

f)
```
   9 4 2
 - 1 8 9
 -------
```

You made it to the end of the book! That's worth celebrating...

Answers

Exercise 1 — pages 2-3

1. a) 531   b) 683   c) 385
   d) 471   e) 893   f) 192

2. a) £1, 10p, £1.10
   b) £6, 10p, £6.10
   c) £3, 60p, £3.60
   d) £4, 7p, £4.07

3. a) false
   b) true
   c) true
   d) false
   e) false

4. a) 603   b) 517   c) 733
   d) 242   e) 433   f) 211
   g) 934   h) 821   i) 314

5. a) 672   b) 386   c) 291
   d) 792   e) 571   f) 488
   g) 281   h) 393   i) 851

Exercise 2 — pages 4-5

1. a) 4   b) 3   c) 2
   d) 4   e) 3   f) 12
   g) 4   h) 10   i) 4

2. a) 691   b) 862   c) 283
   d) 361   e) 485   f) 197
   g) 552   h) 194   i) 762

3. a) 589   b) 796   c) 879
   d) 687   e) 949   f) 469

4. a) £2.10
   b) £1.60
   c) £1.26
   d) £3.05

5. a) 10   b) 5   c) 10
   d) 5   e) 4   f) 10

Exercise 3 — pages 6-7

1. a) 4027   b) 3871
   c) 9519   d) 8492
   e) 2907   f) 1399
   g) 2628   h) 7662

2. The boxes should be ticked for:
   b), d) and f)

3. a) £1.30
   b) £6.10
   c) £1.07
   d) £1.08

4. a) 400
   b) 900
   c) 700
   d) 700
   e) 900
   f) 600

5. a) 8464   b) 1141
   c) 4970   d) 9291
   e) 3614   f) 9365

Exercise 4 — pages 8-9

1. a) two hundred and seven
   b) four hundred and fifty-nine
   c) five hundred and thirty-four
   d) nine hundred and sixty-one

2. a) −   b) +
   c) −   d) −
   e) +   f) +

3. a) 10   b) 8   c) 2
   d) 2   e) 2   f) 11
   g) 5   h) 6   i) 2

4. a) 685   b) 357   c) 468
   d) 846   e) 771   f) 119
   g) 424   h) 532   l) 203

5. a) 242
   b) 478
   c) 357
   d) 995
   e) 860
   f) 709

Exercise 5 — pages 10-11

1. a) 3610   b) 2030
   c) 2390   d) 1890
   e) 5560   f) 7200
   g) 8240   h) 4850

2. a) four hundred and twenty-one
   b) six hundred and fifteen
   c) five hundred and thirty-two
   d) three hundred and eighty-nine
   e) nine hundred and fifty-six

3. a) 481   b) 682   c) 791
   d) 193   e) 862   f) 584
   g) 994   h) 364   i) 495

4. a) 1   b) 6   c) 7
   d) 8   e) 1   f) 5
   g) 8   h) 4   i) 7

5. a) 5700   b) 3230
   c) 8520   d) 4350
   e) 7160   f) 6390

Exercise 6 — pages 12-13

1. a) 721   b) 543   c) 853
   d) 965   e) 445   f) 263

2. a) 404   b) 10
   c) 5460   d) 285
   e) 954   f) 6960

3. a) 5138   b) 7534
   c) 2262   d) 8000
   e) 2000   f) 5000

4. a) 673   b) 488   c) 246
   d) 872   e) 595   f) 378

5. a) 541   b) 721   c) 461
   d) 653   e) 841   f) 324
   g) 242   h) 944   i) 731

Exercise 7 — pages 14-15

1. a) 3140   b) 6230
   c) 2867   d) 8954
   e) 5553   f) 4521

2. a) 651   b) 743   c) 423
   d) 532   e) 226   f) 324

3. a) five hundred and forty-two
   b) four hundred and ninety-four
   c) six hundred and forty
   d) eight hundred and fifty-seven
   e) two hundred and five

4. a) 6   b) 4   c) 10
   d) 21   e) 4   f) 12
   g) 5   h) 27   i) 4

5. a) 7523   b) 6818
   c) 8707   d) 9126
   e) 4543   f) 3794

Exercise 8 — pages 16-17

1. a) 804   b) 306   c) 615
   d) 429   e) 537   f) 709

2. a) 4040   b) 3870
   c) 5460   d) 2850
   e) 9540   f) 6960

3. a) 960   b) 4244
c) 6219   d) 4582
e) 1982   f) 500

4. a) £1.10   b) £7.22
c) £1.40   d) £2.26
e) £5.20   f) £6.49
g) £3.22   h) £3.25

5. a) 629   b) 426   c) 236
d) 509   e) 945   f) 138
g) 808   h) 229   i) 425

Exercise 9 — pages 18-19

1. a) <   b) >   c) >
d) <   e) >   f) <
g) >   h) >   i) <

2. a) 219   b) 518   c) 325
d) 638   e) 408   f) 129

3. a) 1834   b) 6179
c) 6983   d) 6239
e) 3816   f) 1349

4. a) 7   b) 4   c) 9
d) 4   e) 2   f) 4

5. a) 400, 500, 600
b) 95, 130, 350
c) 843, 865, 870
d) 634, 637, 638
e) 611, 752, 863
f) 448, 587, 831

Exercise 10 — pages 20-21

1. a) 388   b) 465   c) 166
d) 559   e) 289   f) 658

2. a) true   b) false
c) true   d) true
e) false   f) false

3. a) 532   b) 441   c) 922
d) 651   e) 823   f) 422
g) 723   h) 563   i) 392

4. a) £3.50   b) £9.22
c) £1.94   d) £8.80
e) £5.31   f) £3.93
g) £7.69   h) £7.76

5. a) 458   b) 585   c) 669
d) 589   e) 173   f) 586
g) 375   h) 454

Exercise 11 — pages 22-23

1. a) 54   b) 24   c) 90
d) 36   e) 63   f) 30
g) 72   h) 72   i) 42

2. a) 800   b) 300   c) 600
d) 900   e) 700   f) 800
g) 100   h) 500   i) 400

3. a) 779   b) 566   c) 189
d) 477   e) 387   f) 676
g) 279   h) 778   i) 386

4. a) 6321   b) 1773
c) 8814   d) 1640
e) 9281   f) 5000

5. a) 9   b) 6   c) 9
d) 11   e) 4   f) 12
g) 9   h) 8   i) 3

Exercise 12 — pages 24-25

1. a) 662   b) 191   c) 473
d) 629   e) 417   f) 926

2. a) 27   b) 48   c) 108
d) 60   e) 45   f) 66
g) 81   h) 99   i) 36

3. a) 40p   b) £1.10
c) 50p   d) £2.50
e) £6.00   f) £1.60

4. a) 998
b) 617
c) 550
d) 307
e) 1000

5. a) 194   b) 817   c) 597
d) 555   e) 449   f) 780

Exercise 13 — pages 26-27

1. a) 35   b) 16   c) 70
d) 32   e) 49   f) 48
g) 77   h) 64   i) 84

2. a) 181   b) 271   c) 591
d) 685   e) 380   f) 974

3. a) 246, 345, 426, 598
b) 431, 513, 675, 896
c) 168, 289, 605, 608
d) 123, 144, 356, 569

4. a) 6450   b) 2160
c) 4780   d) 9080
e) 7370   f) 6230

5. a) 7   b) 2   c) 28
d) 72   e) 10   f) 48
g) 8   h) 24   i) 84

Exercise 14 — pages 28-29

1. a) 8770
b) 1930
c) 3670
d) 2860
e) 6540

2. a) 88   b) 8   c) 4
d) 12   e) 11   f) 10
g) 63   h) 3   i) 5

3. a) 1120   b) 9340
c) 996   d) 3539
e) 1730   f) 1134

4. a) 431   b) 309   c) 543
d) 624   e) 1019   f) 221
g) 859   h) 910   i) 715

5. a) 1270   b) 9870   c) 3250
d) 8720   e) 4090   f) 7130
g) 5960   h) 2690   i) 1400

Exercise 15 — pages 30-31

1. a) 911   b) 421   c) 652
d) 243   e) 344   f) 718

2. a) 9840   b) 1570   c) 8230
d) 2310   e) 7210   f) 3920

3. a) 109   b) 519   c) 226
d) 838   e) 309   f) 409
g) 908   h) 627   i) 718

4. a) 6   b) 9   c) 11
d) 9   e) 4   f) 5
g) 9   h) 8   i) 12

5. a) 211   b) 422   c) 521
d) 643   e) 301   f) 720

Exercise 16 — pages 32-33

1. a) 414   b) 41
c) 578   d) 13
e) 3   f) 34
g) 40   h) 297

2. a) 721   b) 420   c) 540
d) 221   e) 322   f) 714

3. a) 72   b) 8   c) 88
d) 35   e) 24   f) 10
g) 9   h) 42   i) 80

76

4. a) 567, 444, 235, 156
b) 987, 986, 887, 886
c) 634, 589, 432, 321
d) 865, 756, 586, 568

5. a) 24   b) 136
c) 194   d) 21
e) 103   f) 176

Exercise 17 — pages 34-35

1. a) £5.23
    £5.23, £6.13
b) £7.45
    £7.45, £8.07
c) £9.35
    £9.35, £9.81

2. a) 531   b) 54
c) 33   d) 102

3. a) 3460   b) 8900   c) 7660
d) 1740   e) 1250   f) 6750

4. a) 172   b) 416   c) 717
d) 619   e) 518   f) 941

5. a) £7.54
    £7.54, £8.03
b) £8.21
    £8.21, £9.10
c) £3.67
    £3.67, £4.03

Exercise 18 — pages 36-37

1. a) 783   b) 891   c) 914
d) 616   e) 981   f) 482

2. a) £5.45
    £5.45, £6.17
b) £3.86
    £3.86, £4.01

3. a) 4   b) 5   c) 12
d) 4   e) 11   f) 6
g) 4   h) 8   i) 3

4. a) 278   b) 392   c) 498
d) 693   e) 791   f) 878
g) 394   h) 184   i) 592

5. a) 976   b) 614   c) 913
d) 719   e) 651   f) 921

Exercise 19 — pages 38-39

1. a) 60   b) 33   c) 132
d) 88   e) 84   f) 108

2. a) 671   b) 692   c) 938
d) 771   e) 916   f) 655

3. a) 175   b) 179
c) 313   d) 124
e) 106   f) 218
g) 482   h) 237

4. a) 54   b) 3   c) 9
d) 8   e) 6   f) 12

5. a) 11   b) 11   c) 6
d) 2   e) 12   f) 11
g) 12   h) 12   i) 55

Exercise 20 — pages 40-41

1. a) 880   b) 970
c) 690   d) 770
e) 890   f) 910
g) 820   h) 720
i) 830   j) 960

2. a) 66   b) 48   c) 120
d) 77   e) 33   f) 96

3. a) £6.10   b) £8.20
c) £8.52   d) £10.31
e) £2.11   f) £7.01

4. a) three hundred and eighteen
b) one hundred and forty-two
c) two hundred and fifty-eight
d) three hundred and ninety-four
e) six hundred and twenty-seven

5. a) 840   b) 790
c) 770   d) 910
e) 860   f) 950

Exercise 21 — pages 42-43

1. a) £2.40,
    £2.40, £1.90
b) £4.13,
    £4.13, £3.53

2. a) 770   b) 900
c) 740   d) 820
e) 510   f) 920

3. a) 912   b) 867   c) 714
d) 791   e) 781   f) 846
g) 862   h) 939   i) 858

4. a) 7   b) 12   c) 7
d) 8   e) 7   f) 8

5. a) £0.45   b) £1.91
c) £8.45   d) £2.96
e) £5.72   f) £2.94

Exercise 22 — pages 44-45

1. a) 531   b) 931   c) 823
d) 937   e) 813   f) 761

2. a) £4.10
b) £1.41
c) £1.16

3. a) 22   b) 36   c) 60
d) 12   e) 11   f) 12

4. a) 2270   b) 5330
c) 6240   d) 1170
e) 7820   f) 6920
g) 9240   h) 8000

5. a) 643   b) 712   c) 433
d) 936   e) 831   f) 924

Exercise 23 — pages 46-47

1. a) <   b) >   c) <
d) <   e) >   f) <
g) >   h) <   i) >

2. a) 11   b) 12   c) 11
d) 8   e) 48   f) 12

3. a) 970   b) 790
c) 980   d) 630
e) 760   f) 810

4. a) 621   b) 526   c) 322
d) 261   e) 315   f) 461

5. a) $\frac{1}{5}$, $\frac{2}{5}$, $\frac{4}{5}$ b) $\frac{1}{8}$, $\frac{3}{8}$, $\frac{5}{8}$

c) $\frac{2}{7}$, $\frac{3}{7}$, $\frac{5}{7}$ d) $\frac{1}{4}$, $\frac{2}{4}$, $\frac{3}{4}$

e) $\frac{1}{9}$, $\frac{5}{9}$, $\frac{8}{9}$ f) $\frac{4}{12}$, $\frac{7}{12}$, $\frac{10}{12}$

Exercise 24 — pages 48-49

1. a) 280   b) 480   c) 80
d) 150   e) 560   f) 360
g) 220   h) 900   i) 630

2. The boxes should be ticked for:
a), b), f), g), h) and j).

3. a) £3.80   b) £0.99
c) £4.56   d) £1.80
e) £0.66   f) £1.77

4. a) 125   b) 173
c) 36   d) 169
e) 213   f) 242
g) 187   h) 338

5. a) 60   b) 300   c) 360
d) 360   e) 240   f) 490
g) 240   h) 660   i) 200

Exercise 25 — pages 50-51

1. a) 35   b) 64   c) 11   d) 43
e) 21   f) 24   g) 11   h) 11

2. a) 30   b) 100   c) 240
d) 720   e) 700   f) 120
g) 160   h) 240   i) 400

3. a) 834   b) 823   c) 933
d) 720   e) 941   f) 921

4. a) £6.90   b) £6.50
c) £8.49   d) £9.29
e) £6.06   f) £9.00
g) £7.18   h) £7.24

5. a) 13   b) 15   c) 15   d) 31
e) 26   f) 12   g) 24   h) 37

Exercise 26 — pages 52-53

1. a) 5200
b) 1600
c) 2500
d) 6000
e) 9000
f) 4000

2. a) 15   b) 38   c) 20   d) 23
e) 11   f) 23   g) 13   h) 19

3. a) <   b) >   c) <
d) <   e) >   f) <
g) >   h) >   i) >

4. a) 617   b) 914   c) 961
d) 682   e) 919   f) 819

5. a) 8500, 9000
b) 2900, 3000
c) 3500, 3000
d) 1400, 1000

Exercise 27 — pages 54-55

1. a) ×   b) ÷   c) ×
d) ÷   e) ×   f) ×
g) ×   h) ÷   i) ÷

2. a) 8800, 9000   b) 3900, 4000
c) 5400, 5000   d) 1700, 2000
e) 6600, 7000   f) 4300, 4000
g) 7600, 8000   h) 2800, 3000

3. a) $\frac{7}{10}, \frac{5}{10}, \frac{3}{10}$ b) $\frac{3}{4}, \frac{2}{4}, \frac{1}{4}$
c) $\frac{4}{5}, \frac{3}{5}, \frac{2}{5}$ d) $\frac{8}{9}, \frac{5}{9}, \frac{3}{9}$

4. a) 890   b) 600
c) 910   d) 820
e) 830   f) 850
g) 630   h) 660

5. a) 11   b) 9   c) 30
d) 10   e) 3   f) 7
g) 96   h) 12   i) 7

Exercise 28 — pages 56-57

1. a) 4   b) 3   c) 3
d) 10   e) 12   f) 5
g) 4   h) 5   i) 5

2. a) £5.40   b) £2.90
c) £8.92   d) £4.94
e) £1.90   f) £3.88
g) £3.09   h) £3.94

3. a) 12   b) 54   c) 13   d) 23
e) 43   f) 23   g) 24   h) 27

4. a) 11   b) 12   c) 4
d) 2   e) 12   f) 11
g) 11   h) 3   i) 66

5. a) 7   b) 7   c) 4
d) 5   e) 9   f) 3
g) 4   h) 9   i) 7

Exercise 29 — pages 58-59

1. a) 38   b) 49   c) 19   d) 29
e) 69   f) 28   g) 19   h) 6

2. a) 10   b) 8   c) 12
d) 9   e) 3   f) 5

3. The boxes should be ticked for:
a), d), e) and f).

4. a) 20   b) 36   c) 10
d) 44   e) 6   f) 63
g) 5   h) 72   i) 60

5. a) 8   b) 19   c) 9   d) 16
e) 39   f) 18   g) 27   h) 46

Exercise 30 — pages 60-61

1. a) 3, 9   b) 8, 16   c) 4, 16
d) 8, 40   e) 5, 25   f) 9, 72

2. a) 18   b) 16   c) 29   d) 18
e) 8   f) 19   g) 16   h) 29

3. a) 72   b) 21   c) 10
d) 20   e) 5   f) 88
g) 11   h) 132   i) 12

4. a) 811   b) 740   c) 422
d) 921   e) 947   f) 552

5. a) 70   b) 15   c) 20
d) 30   e) 16   f) 18

Exercise 31 — pages 62-63

1. a) 135   b) 148   c) 326
d) 361   e) 235   f) 167

2. a) 60   b) 200   c) 540
d) 4   e) 2   f) 30

3. a) 27   b) 34   c) 19   d) 28
e) 29   f) 8   g) 19   h) 7

4. a) 4, 8   b) 4, 12   c) 8, 32
d) 7, 35   e) 3, 21   f) 4, 20

5. a) 539   b) 190   c) 22
d) 91   e) 128   f) 391

Exercise 32 — pages 64-65

1. a) 20   b) 40   c) 90
d) 50   e) 30   f) 60
g) 80   h) 110   i) 60

2. a) 90   b) 419   c) 85
d) 214   e) 146   f) 125

3. a) 2   b) 420   c) 80
d) 480   e) 12   f) 70
g) 80   h) 1320   i) 8

4. The boxes should be ticked for:
a), d), f) and h)

5. a) 40   b) 40   c) 30
d) 40   e) 120   f) 90

78

Exercise 33 — pages 66-67

1. a) >   b) >   c) <
   d) <   e) >   f) <
   g) >   h) >   i) <

2. a) 51   b) 23   c) 13   d) 25

3. a) 9   b) 10
   c) 20   d) 16
   e) 60   f) 80

4. a) 20   b) 120   c) 90
   d) 80   e) 70   f) 50

5. a) $\frac{1}{7}$, $\frac{1}{5}$, $\frac{1}{4}$ b) $\frac{1}{9}$, $\frac{1}{6}$, $\frac{1}{3}$

   c) $\frac{1}{8}$, $\frac{1}{6}$, $\frac{1}{4}$ d) $\frac{1}{10}$, $\frac{1}{5}$, $\frac{1}{2}$

   e) $\frac{1}{25}$, $\frac{1}{15}$, $\frac{1}{12}$ f) $\frac{1}{10}$, $\frac{1}{9}$, $\frac{1}{8}$

Exercise 34 — pages 68-69

1. a) 3900   b) 4500
   c) 7700   d) 6200
   e) 9100   f) 9100

2. a) $\frac{1}{3}$ b) $\frac{1}{6}$ c) $\frac{1}{2}$
   d) $\frac{1}{4}$ e) $\frac{1}{50}$ f) $\frac{1}{11}$

3. a) 1200
   b) 7000
   c) 1000
   d) 100
   e) 3000

4. a) 147   b) 473   c) 384
   d) 323   e) 791   f) 117

5. a) 8000   b) 5800
   c) 8100   d) 8900
   e) 2900   f) 4300

Exercise 35 — pages 70-71

1. a) 3   b) 6   c) 7
   d) $\frac{4}{5}$ e) $\frac{5}{6}$ f) $\frac{9}{10}$
   g) $\frac{11}{15}$ h) $\frac{12}{17}$ i) $\frac{17}{20}$

2. a) 70   b) 9   c) 210
   d) 8   e) 80   f) 300

3. a) 12   b) 11   c) 9
   d) 12   e) 9   f) 5

4. a) 6100   b) 9000
   c) 9200   d) 8100
   e) 9700   f) 9300

5. a) 2   b) 1   c) 7
   d) $\frac{1}{6}$ e) $\frac{2}{7}$ f) $\frac{9}{13}$
   g) $\frac{8}{19}$ h) $\frac{3}{20}$ i) $\frac{19}{25}$

Exercise 36 — pages 72-73

1. a) 177   b) 199   c) 266
   d) 257   e) 229   f) 295

2. a) $\frac{7}{10}$ b) $\frac{4}{9}$ c) $\frac{10}{11}$
   d) $\frac{3}{7}$ e) $\frac{7}{17}$ f) $\frac{14}{15}$

3. a) 9200   b) 1900
   c) 2500   d) 6000
   e) 1800   f) 2700

4. The boxes should be ticked for:
   a), b), e), and g).

5. a) 69   b) 196   c) 249
   d) 359   e) 147   f) 753